BASEMENT FINISHING SCIENCE

What to Have Done... and *Why*

Lawrence Janesky

Basement Finishing Science
What to Have Done... *and Why*

by Lawrence Janesky
graphic design & editing by Wendy Vandersluis
art directed by Dan Fitzgerald

Published by:
Total Basement Finishing, Inc.
60 Silvermine Road, Seymour, CT 06483
800-816-9766
203-881-5090
www.totalbasementfinishing.com
www.basementsystems.com

ISBN 978-0-9776457-3-2

1st Edition

This book is dedicated to the fine, hard working people at Total Basement Finishing dealerships across North America who help people discover greater living space in below ground environments everyday.

Table of Contents

Foreword

This is not a do-it-yourself book because finishing a below ground space to last is not a do-it-yourself project. It takes too much specialized knowledge, skill, equipment and materials.

The purpose of this book is to give you enough knowledge to make an educated decision on how to have the basement in your home finished, who to do it, and why.

I nearly called this book "How to have your basement finished for the last time." "For the last time"? What does that mean?

That is the great question.

Anyone with a hammer and a saw can finish a basement. Perhaps. But can anyone with a knife operate on you? I guess that depends on what your goals are. What are your expectations and what results do you want to achieve long term? We'll explore the question thoroughly and you can come to your own conclusion.

What makes me an expert?

Twenty six years ago, I graduated high school and started working as a self-employed carpenter. I learned a lot and built my first of twenty-three homes when I was eighteen. I dutifully finished many basements when I was asked. But I did it wrong then. It's funny how good people can do the wrong thing when they don't know it's the wrong thing to do. But alas, time reveals the truth. In 1987,

when the housing bubble of the late eighties burst, I had to find something else to do, since it seemed that going back to smaller remodeling jobs was going backwards. The last home I built had a water problem in the basement. While this case was minor (a wall crack in an unfinished basement), everyone involved made a big deal about it and nobody seemed to know just what to do. My life took a meaningful turn.

From the basement bars and "Summer Kitchens" of the 1950's (now nearly all ripped out) to the full scale use of basements as living space today, the idea of a finished basement is not new. Until recently, not a lot of new thinking has been applied. Ironically, some of the new solutions by some "reputable" names may not provide you with the outcome you wanted for your basement. Now it's time for Basement Finishing to come of age.

CAUTION

Watch out for old ideas. They're still offered and don't work in your basement environment.

20 Years ago, I started a basement waterproofing business called Basement Systems. Today, with 350 dealers in 6 countries who use our products and methods, we are widely recognized as the leader in basement waterproofing and dirt crawl space repair. I have 24 patents on products used in basements and crawl spaces and many more pending. We have been awarded 17 innovation prizes, awards for Business Integrity, Quality, and even been named one of the 10 Best Places to Work in our state by the 170 employees who work in our facility. It has truly been a great success story, and we continue to "break the mold" (pun intended). Check us out on the web at **www.basementsystems.com**

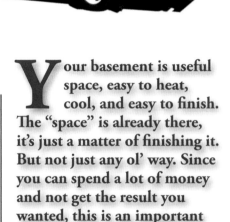

We learn from our dealers and distill the best of the best ideas for products, methods, systems, and ways of doing just about everything in the course of running a business that fixes basement and crawl spaces. I have been an avid learner of "Building Science" since 1987 when I started and even fixed 4,000 homes with radon problems in the air and water.

I have written 3 books besides this one; ***"Dry Basement Science", "Dirt Crawl Spaces: America's Housing Epidemic", and "Crawl Space Science"*** (available at amazon.com).

I have seen thousands upon thousands of basements that were finished. Some done well, most poorly, but all vulnerable to the inevitable enemy that will come in a basement – water, in whatever form. And it does not have to be a "wet" basement for the finished job to be destroyed and rendered an interior wasteland (read on).

I know what not to do extremely well. After seeing so much of the problem, I knew I would recognize the solution when it comes along – and it did.

In 2007, I met Bob Showers (far left) from Pennsylvania and his right hand man Chris Schmidt. They recently developed the wall solution presented in this book. The irony is that there are many firms that specialize in "Finishing Basements". But after being an avid and active building industry participant and observer, long time participant of the National Builders Show and other shows, and reading many trade journals for over 20 years, I have not seen an approach that would solve the problems of durability over time that the Total Basement Finishing System does.

Your basement is useful space, easy to heat, cool, and easy to finish. The "space" is already there, it's just a matter of finishing it. But not just any ol' way. Since you can spend a lot of money and not get the result you wanted, this is an important subject.

And if it's worth finishing your basement at all, it is certainly worth fixing right.

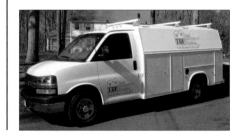

Your local Total Basement Finishing dealer may have given you this book. Otherwise, find your local Total Basement Finishing dealer by calling the *international headquarters* at 1-800-816-9766 or visit www.totalbasementfinishing.com.

Why I wrote this book -

Bob Showers and I teamed up to bring this great solution to homeowners everywhere. So yes, I have an interest in its success. But there is more information that you will need that can't be provided in a brochure, and the issue deserves more attention than that. When confronted with doing a project, most people would want to know what a foremost expert in the field would do in their position.

It is my intention to give you all the facts and ask all the questions you should be asking when undertaking a basement finishing project. I'll present what is available on the market from my company and others and explore the advantages, disadvantages and why they are important. We'll look at waterproofing, walls, ceilings, flooring, windows and other options.

I understand that you're reading this book because you are probably shopping for a finished basement. I am the author, and while I am the owner of a basement finishing company, you are the owner of your home and are the one to make the decision. As with any choice in products, some are not what they promise, and it may be what you don't know that creates a problem for you if you purchase it. This book is full disclosure of the industry for your consideration.

I hope you get value from this information no matter what you decide to do. I respect that you are the judge.

Larry Janesky

April 2008

iii

How to Use this Book
A Reader's Guide

There are 10 brief chapters, each dealing with a specific aspect of finishing your basement. (See the Table of Contents). There are photographs and sidebars in each chapter to help communicate a point. In addition, there are 10 different symbols which have different meanings:

This is especially important to prevent mold.

Apples & Oranges

The two products or systems discussed are very different.

Important

This is important!

Additional Information

This is a BIG IDEA!

This subject is very important in getting the results you want.

You'll Love This!

You will love the results from this!

CAUTION

Beware, don't make this mistake.

Trade Secrets

Insider Information

This is industry insider information.

Important for the resale value of your home.

Important if you want your finished basement to last a long time and don't want to do it twice or more

Terms of the Trade

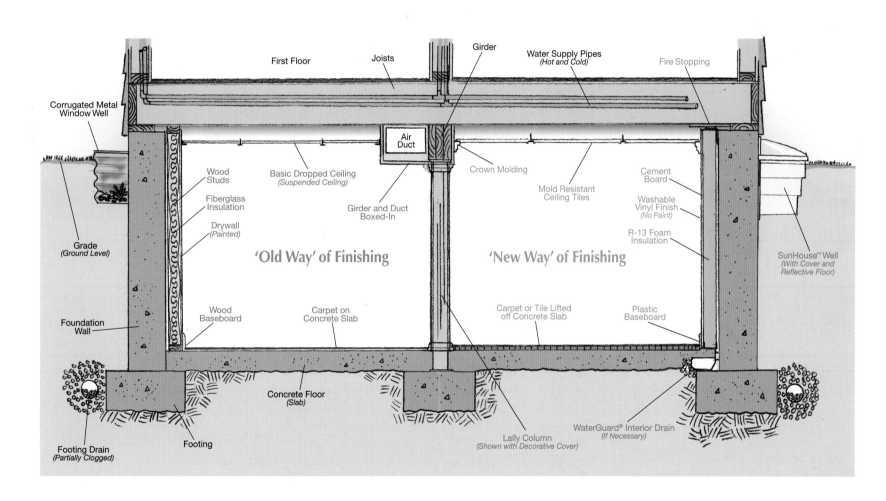

First Floor

Joists

Girder

Water Supply Pipes
(Hot and Cold)

Fire Stopping

Corrugated Metal
Window Well

Air
Duct

Wood
Studs

Basic Dropped Ceiling
(Suspended Ceiling)

Crown Molding

Mold Resistant
Ceiling Tiles

Cement
Board

Fiberglass
Insulation

Girder and Duct
Boxed-In

Washable
Vinyl Finish
(No Paint)

Drywall
(Painted)

'Old Way' of Finishing

'New Way' of Finishing

R-13 Foam
Insulation

Grade
(Ground Level)

SunHouse™ Well
*(With Cover and
Reflective Floor)*

Foundation
Wall

Wood
Baseboard

Carpet on
Concrete Slab

Carpet or Tile Lifted
off Concrete Slab

Plastic
Baseboard

Concrete Floor
(Slab)

Footing Drain
(Partially Clogged)

Footing

Lally Column
(Shown with Decorative Cover)

WaterGuard® Interior Drain
(If Necessary)

Chapter 1

Your basement is important and valuable space!

Mrs. Ohder had the local fireman finish her basement years ago on his time off. It was space she did not need anymore since the kids were gone and she was alone. But she looked forward to selling her home and living off the equity. The real estate agent cringed when Mrs. Ohder said that her house should be worth more, what with a finished basement and all. "Yes, usually," the agent said. Potential buyer after potential buyer one by one came through, but no offers. Finally an offer! But it was very low for a few reasons. Chief among them – they had to "re-do" the musty basement. Her wiser older brother agreed, and she took the offer. It turns out that not just any finished basement space increases the value of a home.

Mr. and Mrs. Lowbal wanted to finish their basement for more living space so they could spread out a little. They got a few estimates. "The lowest price wins our business!" he told his wife. Surely he was no sucker and he was going to keep it that way. So Billy Doright, carpenter extraordinaire, hammered, drywalled, and painted for what seemed like forever. It wasn't exactly Mrs. Lowbal's dream space, but it would have to do. "Come look at our new finished basement!" Mrs. Lowbal said to her friend as she bounded down the stairs with high hopes. "What do you think?" After a pause, an "Oh", and a forced smile, it was the last time she invited anyone to see it. Her baby was ugly.

"Never flooded once in 19 years" Mr. LeKee said to the contractor that was going to finish his basement. The contractor sighed in relief as he scheduled the work. The studs and drywall worked just fine upstairs and Mr. LeKee was anxious to get the basement done for a home theater and lounge. He sure loved the new space! "I have a new DVD from NetFlix" he called to his wife as he descended the stairs. The last step was a doozy. 1½ inches of water in the basement had been sucked up the drywall-which wasn't so dry but *was* a lot ruined. "We're in a drought!" he murmured in disbelief. "Where is it coming from?" "Happens all the time," his plumber friend told him. "Water heaters, washing machines, supply lines. It all winds up in the basement. I'll go get my tools." The finishing contractor was happy to get two jobs in one home. Poor Mr. LeKee!

Mr. and Mrs. Spore moved to their new-to-them home. They knew the basement "had some issues", but felt they could deal with that later. After some time, two of the children began having asthma-like symptoms. When they went to school, they felt better. When they came home, they puffed up again, and stuff leaked from their faces. What was in the home that was causing it? After hiring an indoor air quality consultant, they found the cause – mold in the basement. "We can get rid of the mold", the expert said. "Will it grow back?" Mr. Spore choked out as he saw the bill. "It's possible, I can't guarantee that," the consultant said. And so it did. Mrs. Spore dealt with the mold issue by having her pediatrician prescribe great allergy drugs to keep the symptoms at bay.

Mr. Gill wanted some space to call his own. The kids were getting bigger and taking up lots of space upstairs. He hired a basement finishing company with a special system and a big name. "What about the water that comes in a little every few years? Can you fix that?" "Don't worry. Keep your gutters clean and extend the downspouts and you should be fine," the salesman said. "In fact, that's the best part of our system – it breathes so the walls can dry out and you can remove our panels to fix a leak". "Makes perfect sense to me," Mr. Gill said. One crisp morning after a storm when the basement was complete, Mr. Gill ran down into the basement to gaze at his sanctuary for inspiration before heading off to work. He never made it to work. Instead, he spent the day on the phone with his insurance company, only to find out that his newly-finished and even more newly-ruined finished basement was not covered. With the words "groundwater leaks are never covered" ringing in his head, he called the Pink Basement Finishing Company. "Sorry, we never said it would hold up to water," they said. "But the panels are ruined!" Mr. Gill blurted. "Come see for yourself!" "I don't have to. I know what happens when they get wet. Read your warranty. Of course we can redo the job for…let's say……… hello? hello?" Mr. Gill hung up. It was a bad day at the Gill home.

1

You'll Love
This!

Basement Space is easy to heat and cool!

Since your basement is underground, not exposed to freezing cold and wind, and already interior space, it's easy to heat, especially when the walls are insulated properly with R-13 foam insulation. And since it's down in the cool earth, you won't need any air conditioning! With natural gas, heating oil, and electricity prices at all-time highs (and climbing), this is great news. A house addition that sticks out in the wind with it's own cold roof is going to add to your heating and cooling bills significantly.

Make sense?

Your basement is the least expensive way to increase living space.

When you want more space, you have a few options.

1. Move to a bigger house.

2. Add an addition.

3. Finish the basement.

More Space - Bargain Price

Whether you should move or not is up to you. Maybe you should. But there's a lot more to that option that you probably want to address. An addition could make sense. But remember you need the yard space to do it, it can't be where the septic system is, and it must be within zoning setbacks from property lines. Since you would have to build a new foundation for your addition, and it needs a roof. It's going to cost a lot more than finishing your basement, make a lot more mess and disruption, and take a lot longer.

Your basement already has a floor, a roof, and structural walls. It's a lot simpler, less expensive, less complicated, and faster to finish the basement. That's why finishing a basement is such a popular way to get more living space.

The First Reason Finishing Your Basement with Total Basement Finishing is a "Green" (Environmentally Responsible) Choice

More and more people are concerned about their impact on the environment. Finishing your basement for more space has a low environmental impact - besides the fact that it is space that requires less to heat and cool. Why?

First of all, for every square foot of finished space you put in the basement, that's one less square foot of lawn or forest you are trading for a square foot of roof. This can only be good, since if all the sun saw on the surface of the earth was asphalt roof, we'd all be dead. When you fly low in an airplane, you can see the rooftops of the homes. You can

see how much of a footprint each home takes up. For every square foot of finished basement there is, we have one less square foot of roof and one more square foot of grass. Grass and forests absorbs the sun's heat, consume carbon dioxide, and create oxygen and carbon. That's good! Roof space heats up and causes us to burn electricity to air condition during the day (carbon dioxide emissions) and its heat into the atmosphere at night. We lose. In the winter a roof is a cold surface above us that cools our living space, so we have to burn more fuel to heat our indoor space. We lose again. By having less roof space, we help restore groundwater levels by having more permeable surfaces on our property. Rain that falls on your lawn goes into the ground. Rain that falls on roofs and hard surfaces is often piped away to storm sewers. Who needs more roof and gutter maintenance anyways? Reduce your footprint on earth – literally. By finishing your basement for more space instead of building an addition, you are getting more space under the same roof space.

It's a "green" thing to do. Population Explosion -
Maybe this is meaningful to you and maybe not, but consider this. 1,000 years ago, there were 310 million people on earth and it took 300 years for the population to double. Now there is over 6.6 billion people and

the 1960 population doubled in just 38 years. We have added 1 billion people in just 12 years. There are more and more people all the time, and the resources the average person uses each day is growing. What we each do as individuals to consume more or fewer resources makes a difference. Fifteen years ago, nobody talked like this or thought of this. But knowing what we know now, we must be aware of how our activity and decisions impacts our environment. One concept of conservation is that doing it once (properly) consumes less resources than doing it over and over. When your basement is finished with the TBF system, it will last 100 years. If you do it with other products or systems that get ruined when they get wet, the basement will have to be refinished an estimated 5 times over 100 years. Doing it once is better for the environment, consumes less resources, and costs you less.

DECIDEDLY GREEN

TBF products are good for the environment - never needing to be replaced! Going GREEN - good for all of us!

Total Basement Finishing is a green choice.

Resale Value

How much return on your investment you get depends on the quality of the finished basement space when you sell. If it's done with drywall and smells, it becomes the sort of space that's not good enough to go down there and use but it's not bad enough to rip out. This is not the kind of space that will endear a prospective buyer to your home. If finishing your basement is worth doing, it's worth doing right.

Expense or Investment?

An expense is when you spend your money and the value is gone. An investment is when you spend your money and get it back in the future along with some other benefit.

When a home is valued, the size of the home is considered. Real estate agents can measure only the finished, heated square footage of a home to calculate the size of the living space.

As a simple example, an 1800 square foot ranch with an unfinished basement is listed for sale as an 1800 square foot home. If two-thirds of the basement was finished, then it would be listed as a 3000 square foot home.

Clearly, a "bigger" home is worth more than a smaller one. And that's why an investment in finishing your basement is a good one. You'll get the benefit of enjoying the finished space while you live there, and get your money back (and more?) when you sell your home in the future.

This kind of thing will not add to the value of your home.

This will.

Your Basement Extra Space for Living!

What can you do with your basement?

Playroom • Billiard Room • Party Room • Family Room/Den/TV Room • Art Room • Teen Bedroom • Home Office • Bedrooms
In-Law Apartment • Home Gym • Potting Room • Model Train Set • Home Theater • Library • Wine Cellar • Extra Bathroom
Sauna • Record Storage • Sewing Room • Basement Bar • Computer Room • Cedar Closet • Arts/Crafts Room

Chapter 2

THE issue (water) and why it will get you.

> ❝ There are three things that destroy materials: water, heat, and ultraviolet radiation. Of these, water is by far the most destructive. ❞

Here's the big issue. Basement Space and upstairs spaces are different. What's the distinction? Water. And it's THE issue in finishing a basement. But before you dismiss the issue because YOU don't have a basement that leaks groundwater, read on. It's not just the obvious groundwater problem that we are talking about.

Important

Sources of moisture in a basement –

Plumbing leaks

Condensation

Groundwater leakage

Vapor Transmission

Wicking

Designed for Failure

1.) Groundwater leaks happen when your basement leaks from a heavy rain. Flooded basements have expensive and disastrous effects on a home. Fixing groundwater leaks is the subject of the next chapter, which is a condensed version of my book "Dry Basement Science".

2.) Plumbing leaks will happen. Your basement is a pit in the ground under your home. Your home has a system of supply pipes pressurized at 45 – 60 pounds per square inch. Something's going to blow someday. And when it does, you can get 500 gallons every hour out of a ½" pipe at 50 psi. There is also a system of drain pipes in your home with openings in it – toilets, sinks, showers, tubs, washing machine drains, etc. just waiting to leak.

When a plumbing leaks happens anywhere in the house, water leaks out and drains into the basement. If you have wood, laminate or carpet flooring, drywall, or wood baseboard, you'll be looking at replacing the flooring, drywall, and repainting, etc.

You hope you'll notice a plumbing leak right away, but unless you go in your basement a lot, it usually goes undetected for a while. By then, the damage is done to conventional materials used for finishing your basement.

Janesky's First Law of Hydrodynamics –

Water flows downhill.

Thus, a leak anywhere in the house floods the basement.

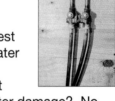

The insurance industry's largest loss is from water damage. And the two largest sources of water damage? No, it's not the great 100 year flood. It's the ubiquitous water heaters and washing machine hoses! In fact there is a whole industry called "Property Restoration Contractors" who do water damage clean-up and rip outs.

3.) Wicking

(also called "capillary action") occurs when water in liquid form soaks through porous materials. Concrete is porous, and when it's wet on one side, it soaks the water to the other side like a sponge. This is common in block walls, but it can also happen to floors and other types of foundation walls.

4.) Vapor Transmission

is when water in vapor form comes through the porous concrete and evaporates off the surface into the basement. A gas, (such as water vapor) will move from more to less. Even when the ground is not saturated, it's near 100% humidity all the time, and that water vapor is moving through the concrete into your basement. This is one reason the basement air feels damp and heavy. The problem is when you put a material against the surface of the floor or walls and trap the water vapor there. When this happens, moisture builds up to

levels where mold can grow. Vapor transmission and condensation are why mold grows in basements that do not leak groundwater when it rains.

5.) Condensation

develops when warm humid summer air enters the basement and is cooled on the basement walls and floor surfaces. The hotter and more humid it is outside, the more of a problem condensation will be.

Condensation: **This is how it works –**

A.) The ground temperature in your area equals the average outdoor air temperature year round. Clearly, that's less than the temperature of summer air.

B.) The house has an upward draft of air caused by heat rising in the house. In the summer, this is caused by solar heating. In winter it is caused by our heating system. As air rises through the house it escapes the upper levels of the home. New air has to enter to replace the air that escaped. That new air enters at the lower levels of the home. Basically, your house is blowing air out the top and sucking air in at the bottom. That's how it sucks hot, humid outside air into the basement in the summertime. ***(See next page.)***

C.) Warm air holds more moisture than cool air. For every degree we cool the air, we raise the relative humidity by 2.2% provided that we don't take any water out of it. If the outside air is 80 degrees and has an 80% Relative Humidity, and it leaks into the basement which is 68 degrees, we've cooled the air by 12 degrees and raised the relative humidity by (12 degrees x 2.2%) 26.4% from where it started at 80% RH. But we can't have over 100% Relative Humidity, so what happens is we get condensation all over the coldest surfaces – the walls and floors-which are dense and cooled by the ground, or air conditioning ducts and cold water pipes.

Condensation can be mild or severe, causing puddles. Either way, this is a BIG distinction between basement space and indoor space, along with the four other sources of moisture listed above. This is why <u>you CAN NOT finish a basement with conventional materials and expect good results.</u>

Didn't my builder waterproof my foundation to prevent water from coming in? The short answer is NO. If you have a good waterproof coating (not just black asphalt) on the outside of your foundation walls and installed a vapor barrier under your floor, congratulations; you are one of the lucky few. The fact is that building codes do not require "waterproofing" on the outside of basement walls as opposed to "damp proofing" (which does very little) or vapor barriers under the floors. (There are exceptions, but only recently and only in a tiny percentage of towns.) When not forced to spend anymore money on one part of the thousands of elements a builder must assemble to create a home, he doesn't do it. It's visible features with bling like nice cabinets, a skylight, or better fixtures that a builder uses to attract buyers. Stuff that goes underground has no bling factor and gets ignored. And that's likely what happened when they built your home.

"No bling-bling, no go"

You breathe basement air even when you're not in the basement.

Prove it!

To show how your house breathes in at the bottom and out at the top, do this test. In the winter, go into your basement and open a window a bit. Feel the cold air blasting in at you? Close the window. Now go upstairs – to the second floor if you have one. Crack open a window an inch or so. You don't feel any cold air blasting in? Why not? Because warm air is blasting OUT. With low air pressure on the lower levels, your house sucks on the ground, then blows air out of the upper levels due to a higher air pressure.

As warm air rises in a home, it leaks out of the upper levels. New air must enter to replace the air that escaped. In fact, in an average home, about half of the air in the home escapes each hour out of the upper levels. This creates a suction at the lower levels of the home to draw in replacement air. In older, leaky homes, the air exchange rate can be as high as a full air exchange per hour.

What this "stack effect" does is create an airflow in your home from bottom to top. Air from the basement is drawn upwards into the first floor, and then to the second floor. Of course, it dilutes with other air in your home, but building scientists say that up to 50% of the air you breathe on the first floor is air that came from the basement. If you have hot air heating with ductwork, the air mixes even more thoroughly throughout the house.

Therefore, whatever is in your basement air is in your house and affecting you, whether you spend much time in the basement or not. If there is high humidity downstairs, there is higher humidity upstairs than there would be otherwise. If there is mold in the basement, there are mold spores upstairs. If there are damp odors downstairs – you get the idea.

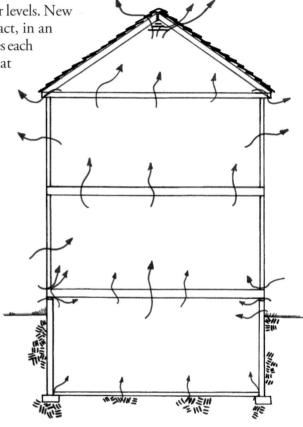

STACK EFFECT

Foundation Types

Stone Walls

- Common in older homes.
- Leaks are always a concern.

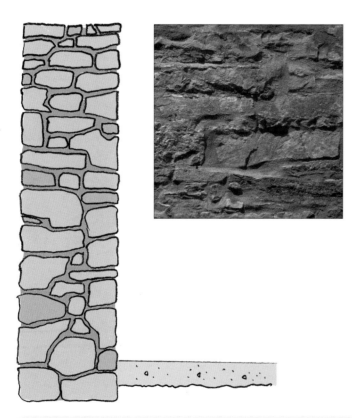

Block Walls

- Most common 1940-1975.
- Used to be made from cinders - "cinder blocks."
- Blocks have been made from concrete for some time.

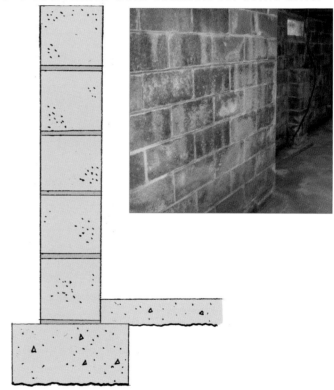

God's gift. Everything is a gift to someone or something. Block walls have been called "God's gift to waterproofing contractors". They offer very little resistance to air and water flowing through them. What I mean is – they leak like crazy. Since they are hollow, when water gets inside them from the outside, it spreads out inside the wall and the whole wall leaks.

Foundation Types (continued)

Poured Concrete Walls

- Most common today.
- Resists water better than block.
- Leaking cracks are a concern.

Monolithic Foundations

- Could be block or poured walls.
- The difference is that the floor and footing are poured in one piece.
- With the walls on top, it's a two-piece foundation instead of a three-piece.

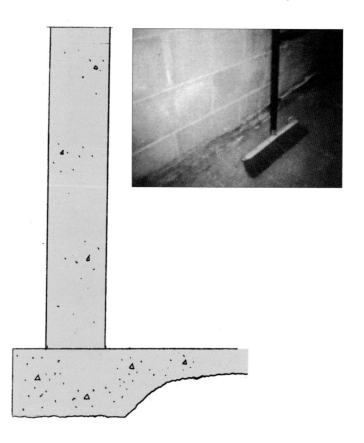

Foundation Types (continued)

Precast Foundation Walls

- Newest idea, still relatively rare.
- Wall resist water penetration.
- Having a great sump pump system is a must!
- Looks like concrete studs inside.

Wood Foundation Walls

- Treated wood stud walls and plywood.
- Very rare in most areas.

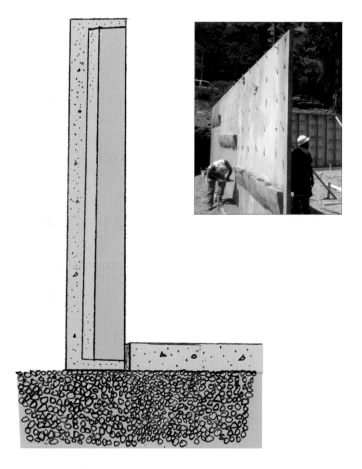

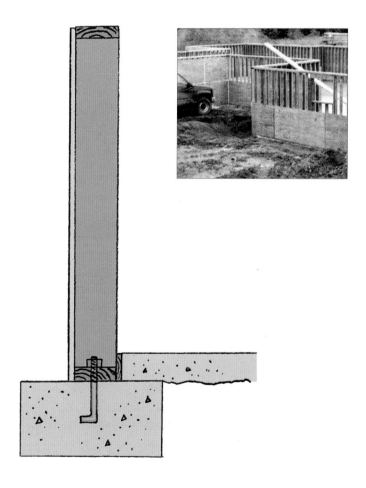

Water + Wood or Paper = BAD.

This is a **BIG IDEA!**

! Important

Side Note

A Concrete Guarantee

There are two things a concrete contractor will guarantee about concrete. It will get hard and it will crack. And of course cracks allow water to flow in. They can be fixed of course, but it's a common problem and a challenge and consideration for a prospective finished basement owner.

Profound Statement -
"If the material once lived, keep it out of your basement."

Organic materials are materials that come from a tree or animal. Wood, plywood, particle board (laminate floor backing), OSB (Oriented Strand Board), cardboard, jute (carpet backing), paper (facing on drywall), and rubber (latex paint) come from trees. Leather and furs come from animals. When organic materials are dead, they need to be turned back into dirt and returned to the earth. How does this happen?

God put mechanisms on the earth to decay organic materials. They are called mold, rot, and bugs. But how do mold, rot, and bugs know when they have a job to do? Why don't they not eat your dining room table but they will attack/live/thrive on organic materials in your basement?

I think you know the answer... **water.**

When a dead tree limb falls to the forest floor, it's damp. Mold, rot, and bugs are triggered to do their thing. Mold, rot and bugs make no distinction between a dead tree limb on the forest floor and a damp 2x4 or paper-faced drywall in your basement. They do their thing.

Profound Statement -
Mold, Rot and Bugs are not interested in "inorganic materials."

Inorganic materials are materials that are from the earth and were not alive at one time (at least not in the last million years). They include minerals such as sand and cement, gypsum, metals, and materials made from petroleum such as vinyl and plastics. Therefore, we should use inorganic materials in an environment that is likely to be wet. And THAT is the moral of the whole finished basement story.

Mold needs 4 things to grow.

1. Spores (seeds of mold)

2. Food (organic material)

3. Water or high humidity

4. Temperature between 32º and 110º F (0º and 43º Celsius)

Mold spores are everywhere. You're breathing some right now. The temperature range 32º-110º F we can't get away from. We kind of like that temperature range too. That leaves food and moisture. We want to eliminate as much of the food as possible in a basement – especially with things that are difficult and expensive to replace like flooring, walls, trim, and finishes. We eliminate as much water as possible by fixing any groundwater leaks, and we dehumidify to control condensation and moisture from vapor through concrete. But we can't stop all water all the time because of plumbing leaks and surprise groundwater leaks from "the big one". That why we have to eliminate the food as well.

Q. *How do you blow tens of thousands of dollars in a day or two without having to be present?*

A. Just add water.

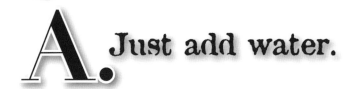

To Your Health
(And if not yours, then theirs)

You can't find a doctor who says mold in a home is good. You can't find a doctor who says mold in your home is "not bad."

It's bad. It's all bad.

Besides irritating people with asthma and mold allergies, studies show that prolonged exposure to mold can actually cause asthma.

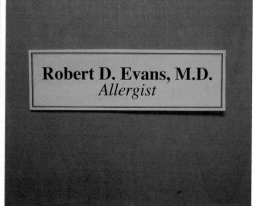

Robert D. Evans, M.D.
Allergist

Why mold is a bigger problem today than 40 years ago.

Important

Is mold really a bigger problem than in the past or is it just that our tolerance for unhealthy spaces has gone way down and our standards for clean living are higher? Well, it's both. We all know that mold is a cause to sound the alarms today. With all the bad press mold has received with lawsuits and health concerns, you can't help but be very concerned when you see it. Don't even try to list your home for sale if you have mold! There's even a disclosure form you must fill out when listing your home now that asks many questions; among them, "Have you ever had any mold?"

2

Mold is a bigger problem than in the past for these reasons:

1. **Drywall.** We used to build homes with plaster walls. There's no paper in plaster like there is in drywall. And paper is "mold candy". Mold will grow on paper faster than on framing lumber because paper is processed (a pre-chewed meal for mold).

Heartwood

2. **The lumber itself.** In the old days, we used old growth trees for lumber. These logs had primarily heartwood. Today we farm fast growing trees for lumber. These logs are mostly sapwood. Mold likes the sugary sapwood much better than heartwood.

Sapwood

3. **Particle board.** Today we use a lot of particle board where we used to use 1 x 8 tongue and groove sheathing or plywood. Mold favors particle board or "chipboard" over the former materials. And when chipboard gets wet, it swells and stays swelled when it dries out. That is why having laminate floors made of particle board with a facing is like playing Russian roulette in your basement. Eventually you'll have a leak. That's all you need, and your laminate floor is done for.

4. **Air conditioning.** 40 years ago, nobody had it. Now everyone does. Back then, we opened windows and equalized the temperature between indoors and outdoors. Now we keep the indoor environment cooler than the outdoors in the summer. In doing so, we have cool surfaces inside for condensation to form on – and that suits mold just dandy. In addition, most air conditioning units are oversized. They cool the air too quickly, satisfying the thermostat and shutting off - not running long enough to dehumidify the indoor air.

"What makes a basement smell like one?"

Answer... MOLD

Mold grows on wet organic materials. To reproduce, it sends off airborne "spores" (seeds) to hopefully land on other wet organic surfaces and grow. These spores are what you smell when a basement is "musty". When mold dries out, it doesn't die but goes "dormant", waiting for the next damp period to have the next party.

Some molds compete for space with other molds by producing mycotoxins, which kill other molds. People who have asthma or are allergic to mold react to these spores. In rare cases, toxic mold can produce very bad reactions in people. Even if you like musty smells and snort mold for fun, it's still not good for your property value because most people don't share that enthusiasm.

Mold doesn't grow underwater.

It doesn't have to be WET for mold to grow – just humid. There are tens of thousands of types of mold. Some grow at lower relative humidity, (65% for example), than others. Relative humidity levels over 80% will surely invite some mold to grow. At over 90% relative humidity, wood will rot. This is why ALL basements need to be finished with inorganic materials even if they don't leak groundwater.

"MicroEnvironments"

Even if it's not 80% Relative Humidity in the middle of your basement room, what about behind the walls and under the flooring where the temperature, drying capacity, and moisture content is different? Mold doesn't grow in the middle of the room. So what matters is the Relative Humidity at the surfaces where mold can grow. Mold could be flourishing behind walls and under flooring even if your basement seems pretty dry.

How many **leaks** does it take to ruin a finished basement? 2

I recall an old TV commercial. A wise owl is asked "How many licks does it take to get to the center of a Tootsie Pop?" The wise owl begins licking and counting "One, Two, Three" and then he bites it. "Three" he declares. Well, I guess it depends when you bite it. A big leak will take you out in one shot. A series of smaller ones will render your basement a space not good enough to be happy with and not bad enough to rip out. That is, of course, if you use conventional materials. I have seen lots of finished basements used for just storage for exactly this reason.

"One, Two..."

Fiberglass

The emperor has no clothes.

I cringe at the thought of fiberglass insulation. It's pitiful and misused and few in the building industry realize it or are willing to admit it. I could go on about this for a long time, but let me give you the high points.

The R rating on fiberglass applies to insulation that is installed in a closed cavity fully fluffed with no air gaps on the sides, front or back. Between drywall and plywood sheathing in an upstairs wall, for example. An example of misuse is when it's installed in a basement ceiling where

Fiberglass is like a sponge!

it is open on one side, with all the pipes, wires and cross-bridging to crinkle it up and create air "burps". Everyone knows air flows through fiberglass like air through cotton candy. It is very seldom installed properly, so you don't get the insulation performance you were promised on the package. Most people that install the stuff don't even understand this. Fiberglass insulation loses a high percentage of its R value when it gets just a small percentage of water in it. And fiberglass gets ruined when it gets wet.

The quicker picker upper". If you took a piece of fiberglass and ran in under the faucet, would it gain weight? Of course, many times over. And it will lose its shape as it gets wet and heavy, and it will flop over in a big wet heap like toilet paper. Right? It's a material that sucks up water, and therefore its not appropriate for a basement. And speaking of paper, most fiberglass insulation has a paper facing on one side. Even foil faced insulation comes with foil laid over paper. And paper is "moldnip".

Fiberglass is made from sand.

What color do you suppose fiberglass is when it comes out of the ground? Bright pink? Bright yellow? No. It's a neutral color. How do you suppose it got these bright colors? Right. Dye. And what do you suppose happens to the dye when the fiberglass gets wet? It leaches out and stains the adjoining materials.

One big company who produces fiberglass, has a system for finishing basements (which others have copied) that uses a fiberglass panel covered with fabric. When it gets wet, it's ruined.

Yes, it bothers me. It bothers me a lot.

People think that just because they have a big, recognizable name and the system is supposedly just for finishing basements, the public will trust them and buy it. They get materials that are inappropriate for a basement. An example comes to mind with one woman I know in Philadelphia bought it. Months later, when she had a significant plumbing leak, and the panels soaked up the water and were ruined. The company said the problem has nothing to

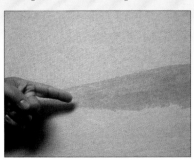

do with them or any warranty and offered to replace the walls for $10,000. Argghhh! What's the sense of having a "Basement Finishing System" if it's going to get ruined in a basement? And further, they claim that moisture will "breathe" through the walls so it doesn't build up and cause mold. Think about this for a moment. The fiberglass walls are supposed to be insulation. If they breathe (air flowing though them, or "convection") then they don't insulate very well. Right? When you touch fiberglass insulation, the little glass fibers stick to you and irritate you right away. Imagine breathing these fibers? Who wants this stuff in their home at all anyway?

There's an old saying...

"When all you have is a hammer, everything looks like a nail." Thus, "When all you make is fiberglass, everything looks like a fiberglass application".

Trade Secrets

Insider Information

Why mold grows on "inorganic" fiberglass

Mold can grow on fiberglass. But wait a minute, fiberglass is inorganic, so how is that possible? The answer is in the resin used to set the fiberglass fibers into a semi-rigid board or batt. The resin is made from urea-based chemicals. "Urea" sounds a lot like pee-pee to me. Well, it is. It's actually cow urine. They use it in manufacturing and it's made from the cow's process of blending organic material (grass and water) with the cows own special something (Don't ask how they collect it). That's why mold grows on fiberglass. To be fair, a little mold can grow on any inorganic material if it's dirty or dusty. But the mold is growing on the dirt not the inorganic material.

Conclusion –

Don't use fiberglass in your basement.

So I don't leave you hanging too long here, I will tell you that the new insulation sensation in the building industry is **closed-cell foam insulation**. The only reason it hasn't replaced fiberglass completely yet is that foam costs more. Since most builders have to be cheapskates to make a profit, the fiberglass industry won't disappear overnight. But as foam manufacturers and installers get their supply chains and efficiencies worked out better... well let's just say I'm glad I don't own a fiberglass plant. And the fiberglass manufacturers know the end of this party is in sight. That's why they are trying to find more and more different applications for fiberglass.

More on foam insulation later. . .

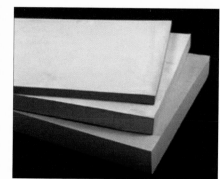

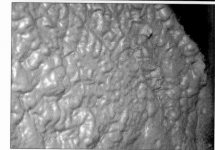

Take the Quiz –

2

Finish the next four thoughts

My optimism (believing my basement will stay dry)
will not change whether my basement gets wet one day.   True   or   False

Mold, rot, and bugs like wet organic
material, even in my house.   True   or   False

Wood, drywall, fiberglass, most carpets, paints, and laminate
floors are organic or have some organic material in them.   True   or   False

I do not want to replace the walls,
flooring, or trim when my basement gets wet.   True   or   False

Answers: All true

Conclusion... Your finished basement will be wet at some point. Don't finish your basement with materials that get ruined by water, high humidity, or the mold that comes along with such an occurence.

Chapter 3

Waterproof it first!
Hope for your wet basement.

(Skip this chapter if you have never had any groundwater and you don't have a sump pump)

If your basement leaks, don't worry.

It can be fixed so you can finish it. This is an area that I and 350 of my closest friends have specialized in for decades. We got this one down.

Basement Systems is the world leader in making below ground spaces dry. We have many exclusive products and processes that we have used, ohhh, 150,000 times. We have exclusive dealers all across the US, Canada and Europe. In some cases, your Total Basement Finishing dealer is the "Basement Systems" dealer as well. In other cases they're not, but they have a close working relationship.

Step 1   Step 2

We can help you.

For complete information, you can get my book "Dry Basement Science", which our dealers make sure each prospective customer has. The more you know, the better for all of us.

The next 6 pages is a summary of what causes a basement to leak, what we can do for you, and why we do it.

What causes your basement to leak?

Answer – Backfill Saturation.

Backfill is the dirt just outside your basement walls.

When it gets saturated, it puts hydrostatic pressure (pressure from the weight of the water at rest) on your walls, and joints between your footings and walls, and the floor/wall joint. Water leaks in. If you have hollow block walls, water leaks into the walls and out from the walls into the basement. If you have stone walls it leaks through the joints between the stones and into the basement at various elevations in the wall. Your basement floor can leak if the water finds its way from the dirt outside to the soil under your basement floor.

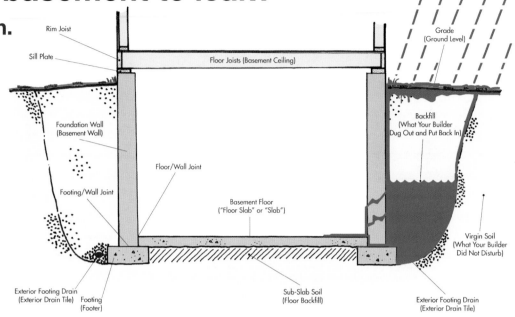

Rim Joist
Sill Plate
Floor Joists (Basement Ceiling)
Grade (Ground Level)
Foundation Wall (Basement Wall)
Backfill (What Your Builder Dug Out and Put Back In)
Floor/Wall Joint
Footing/Wall Joint
Basement Floor ("Floor Slab" or "Slab")
Exterior Footing Drain (Exterior Drain Tile)
Footing (Footer)
Sub-Slab Soil (Floor Backfill)
Virgin Soil (What Your Builder Did Not Disturb)
Exterior Footing Drain (Exterior Drain Tile)

3

Don't I have drains or waterproofing to stop the water?

You may. But usually what was done in the way of drains or wall coatings was done with materials that won't last and protect your finished basement. That's why you are in the mess you're in now. Can you imagine an important assembly in a structure that will not last as long as we expect the structure to? This builds a repair project into the future. Who would do such a thing? Where have I heard this theme before?.....**Hmmm…**

Trade Secrets

Insider Information

How to fix it-

Some people think that you can fix it outside. Well, it's possible, but it's not practical and almost no one does it from the outside anymore because it's expensive, messy, and not serviceable.

But there are things that should be done outside. They include keeping gutters clean, extending downspouts, and making sure the ground pitches away from the house if possible. While these things can make a difference, they can not and will not keep your basement dry. Why? Because they are not responsible for all of the water that leaks into your basement all the time under all conditions. If your finished basement is on the line, with all your furniture and boxes and contents at risk, do you want to rely on your gutters not being frozen or clogged?

THE Solution

There are a few parts of the solution, but the first one is an interior perimeter drainage system called WaterGuard. It captures water from the walls and floor and drains it away to a sump. It is a specially designed piping system just for basement waterproofing. To install it, a trench is created in your basement floor along the wall at the perimeter. The WaterGuard is installed and backfilled with clean drainage stone, and the floor over it is then restored. The WaterGuard has a special wall drain to catch water from any wall leaks higher up on the walls. A vapor barrier can be installed on the wall and tucked into the WaterGuard – the preferred method for a basement that will be finished. This vapor barrier will drain wall leaks down into the WaterGuard without the water touching the back of the wall panels and potentially dripping on the floor in front of the WaterGuard.

Pump it out.

Sounds simple enough. If the WaterGuard collects all the water from the perimeter walls and under the floor, it must drain it somewhere. A sump pump is usually the place. Ancient cartographers used to mark unknown, suspicious lands on their maps with "Here be Dragons". If you don't know a lot about sump systems, this is where your dragon is. But you're in luck! We know all about sump systems and happen to have the world's best. But let me give you some information and you can decide for yourself. Let's pretend you have a sump pump as part of your strategy to keep groundwater from wetting your finished basement when it rains hard.

"Here be dragons!"

Questions you don't have to be an expert to answer –

Q.
- How do you know when the pump fails? • How do you know when the pump is unplugged?
- How do you know when the circuit breaker has tripped?
- What happens when the power goes out (usually in a heavy rain storm)?
- What happens when there is a very heavy rain and one pump can't keep up with the flow of water?
- You are pumping the water to the outside – How do you know the discharge pipe outside has frozen?

A. "Your finished basement gets Flooded!"

So as you can see – any ol' sump pump in any ol' sump hole will not protect your finished basement when something goes wrong!

Do you want your new finished basement dry –

A. Some of the time?
B. Most of the time?
C. All of the time?

I bet I know what you picked!

Here's what I recommend for sump pump equipment to protect your finished basement.

TripleSafe™
SUMP PUMP SYSTEM

It's a system called the TripleSafe Sump System. I developed it in response to seeing so many people who thought they were protected get flooded from pump failure.

The TripleSafe System has 3 pumps.

1. First is a 1/3 horsepower (hp) Zoeller M-53 cast iron primary pump with a mechanical float switch. This pump does most of the pumping most of the time. It is strong, efficient, quiet, and reliable.

2. Next is a ½ hp AC back-up pump – a Zoeller M98. This pump will take over in the event the primary pump fails or can't keep up with the amount of water flowing in. Since both of these pumps are installed with separate discharge pipes to the exterior, you can discharge over twice as much water with your ½ hp AC back-up pump running at the same time as your 1/3 hp primary pump.

3. The third pump is an "UltraSump" Battery Operated (DC) back-up pump. It will operate if the power goes out, or if the circuit breakers for the other pumps trip, because the water will rise and kick the UltraSump on.

3 Pump 3-UltraSump® Battery Back-up Pumping System (Battery and automatic charging system are included)

Pump 2-Zoeller M-98 1/2 hp High Volume Pump

2

Pump 3 operating range

Pump 2 operating range

Pump 1 operating range

1 Pump 1-Zoeller M-53 1/3 hp Pump

You'll Love This!

Triple protection for your finished basement.

If you rely on a pump to keep your basement dry, you need a back-up system. Even if you have a very good sump pump now, you'll need an UltraSump battery operated back-up pump at a very minimum. If you don't have it, you're just waiting for the basement to flood when a pump or power interruption happens. Remember, it's not *if*, it's *when*. All three pumps in the TripleSafe System will not fit in a standard round sump liner. So the TripleSafe has a unique twin liner configuration. The primary pump is on one side with the battery operated UltraSump piggy back on it and the ½ hp AC back-up pump on the other side.

In addition, some other very cool features are built into the system. (Okay, it's my thing, so it's cool to me, but it's important for reliability to you). The pumps sit on pump stands, and keep the pumps out of any silt and sediment.

The TripleSafe has an airtight sump lid, which keeps the pool of water sitting in the sump hole from evaporating into your basement environment. It also keeps stuff from falling in to the sump hole, it's a safety feature when it comes to small children, and it looks a whole lot better than an open, muddy pit cracked in your basement floor. You also save storage space since the lids are strong and you don't have to worry about keeping things away.

Next is a WaterWatch Alarm which will sound off like a smoke detector in the unlikely event that water rises above all pump operating ranges.

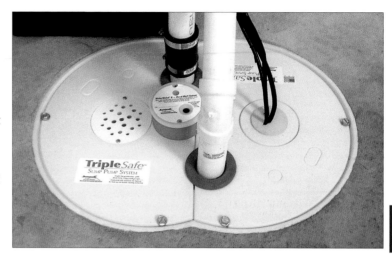

3

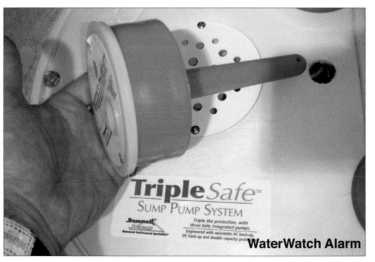

WaterWatch Alarm

The TripleSafe is the best pump protection you can get, (besides two of them for a big basement) save for an automatic generator system for a back-up power supply. That's a whole 'nuther kettle of fish at $10,000 more, but it will run your fridge, lights and furnace in the event of a power outage. And even then, a generator will not help protect you from mechanical pump failures like an extra battery backup pump can.

For most situations, the 12,000 gallons of water the UltraSump pumps out on one fully charged battery is enough to take you through a power outage until the power comes back on.

Will the TripleSafe Sump System eliminate your chances of getting flooded 100%? Is it guaranteed? No, but it will reduce your chances of flooding down to a statistically insignificant number.

There's always another level of protection that you can buy to cover even more circumstances. For most, the TripleSafe makes the most sense and will get you the protection you need for your finished basement.

Besides a WaterGuard drainage system, a TripleSafe pumping system, a vapor barrier on the walls tucked into the WaterGuard System, and extending the downspouts, there is one more important part of the basement waterproofing puzzle - Dehumidification.

Chapter 4

Mastering Humidity - the Anti-Mold

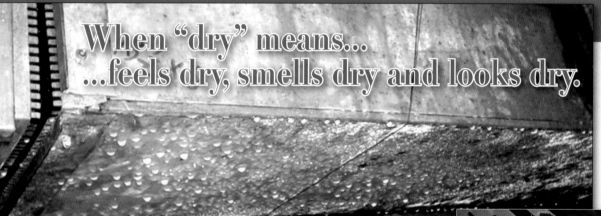

When "dry" means...
...feels dry, smells dry and looks dry.

By now, you know that mold can grow in your finished basement even without a plumbing or groundwater leak because all you need is high Relative Humidity. And High Relative Humidity can be caused by water vapor coming through the

concrete and by condensation. For many folks, when it is hot and humid in the summertime, their basement may be the most damp and smelly it is all year because of condensation against their cool basement floors and walls.

Even without condensation, we still get high relative humidity levels, from water vapor passing through concrete which allows mold to grow and causes "stinky basement syndrome." And dust mites are having a party. More on that later.

In order to eliminate condensation you need to either heat the basement (ridiculous in summer), or take water out of it (easy to do). Correction. I should say take water out of it *efficiently and effectively* (not so easy unless you have the right equipment to do it with).

Not Just Any Dehumidifier

A dehumidifier is the plain answer. But not just any dehumidifier. I have been working this issue over 20 years. The only machine that will keep your finished basement dry and odor free is one called a SaniDry Basement Air System. And it's awesome.

The SaniDry is a high-capacity, high-efficiency dehumidification system, with air filtration in a single unit. The SaniDry takes up to 100 pints (47.3 L) of water per day out of your basement air, while using the same energy as a "40 pint" (18.9 L) dehumidifier. And it filters particles out of the air to less than an incredible two microns in size – which is smaller than any mold spore or dust mite dropping!

You'll *really* Love This!

SaniDry™
Basement Air ≈ System

The SaniDry Basement Air System wrings your air dry, and its powerful blower moves that dry air out into and around your basement space. This dry air then dries your building materials and basement contents, which makes the damp smell and damp feeling go away. What a huge difference a SaniDry can make in "condensation season!" People really love their dry basement environments after having a SaniDry installed.

4

You'll never have to empty any buckets on your SaniDry system because it automatically drains into either your WaterGuard or sump system, or a condensation pump.

Having a groundwater-free basement is one thing. Adding a SaniDry is like putting the cherry on top of your dry basement program. It makes it complete. I haven't seen many basements that <u>don't</u> need one. Picture the concrete in your basement turning white because it's so dry! Sweet!

Wimpy, wimpy, wimpy.   Hefty, Hefty, Hefty.

How does it perform so incredibly well with the same amount of energy that less-effective 20-pound-weakling dehumidifiers use?

Apples & Oranges

1. **The SaniDry blows air over a huge, cold coil. It looks like a truck radiator instead of the little squirrely spiral coil of dinky dehumidifiers.**

2. **The SaniDry runs the exiting dry, cold air through a special heat-exchange core that pre-cools the incoming wet air and recaptures energy.**

3. **The SaniDry's powerful 250 cfm blower not only grabs more air in to dry faster, but it moves the conditioned, dry air out around to dry the contents of your basement.**

Powerful blower. *250 cfm blower really moves dry air around to dry your entire basement!*

4

To further prove its mettle, SaniDry is Energy Star rated – a rare achievement for a dehumidification system. Another big benefit is that it doesn't have to be located in the space it's drying. You can locate it in a utility room and duct the wet air in and dry air out to the main room of your basement.

There is simply no comparison between a SaniDry Basement Air System and any dehumidifier you've ever seen. I am usually a bit conservative and always realistic about what a product can do. The SaniDry is one product where I let all the performance promises hang out.

Damp Dirty Air In

Dry Clean Air Out

A SaniDry faithfully serves a Total Basement Finishing basement from the storage room by ducting the air through the wall.

Save Money:
Dry Air is Easier to Cool!

Damp indoor air costs more money to cool. Sure, a SaniDry costs a bit in electricity to run, but lower cooling costs in part offset this electric cost. This is because your central air system has to remove moisture from the air in order to cool it, and that takes energy. Air conditioning systems are inefficient at dehumidifying. If you dry the air in your basement, that air rises into the rest of the house, making the whole house drier.

SaniDry – Energy Test Winner!

Apples & Oranges

We tested four dehumidifiers to find out the cost per pint of water removed from the air. The worst performer was a standard household unit available under any number of recognizable brand names. It came out at more than 11 cents per pint. A higher priced unit, but one without the features of the SaniDry, cost about 10 cents per pint of water removed. The big winner was the SaniDry, which cost only 3.3 cents per pint of water removed! **What a bargain!**

Did I mention I love the SaniDry system? You will too.

Open Sump Hole?

Having an open sump hole and running a dehumidifier is like trying to fill a bucket with a hole in it. As you dry the air, more water evaporates into it. Why? The open sump hole has a pool of water sitting in it all year. In other words, you have a humidifier to counteract your dehumidifier.

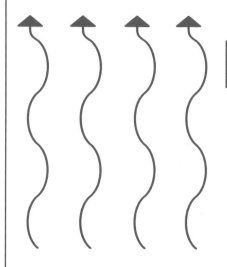

4

Dehumidifiers Should Drain Automatically

Quick – How many hours in a week? 168.

How long would it take a cheapo dehumidifier's bucket to fill up and shut off?
Maybe 12.

If you empty it once a week, what percentage of the time is it actually running? 7% of the time. Meaning it's **off** for **93% of the time.**

Who wants to have "empty dehumidifier bucket" on their daily chore sheet? The answer is to hook it up with a hose to automatically drain the water away – then you never have to empty it.

A condensate pump eliminates emptying buckets.

Keep Basement Windows Closed!

There is no reason to open a basement window for any type of climate control. When the air outside is cooler than inside, you lose heat. When it's warmer outside you bring in moisture.
Keep basement windows closed.

Dust Mites – #1 Indoor Allergen

The number one thing that people with asthma and allergies react to indoors is dust mite droppings. These parasites live in your furniture, bedding, carpeting, and feed off dead skin flakes. Their droppings are so small that they become airborne, are breathed in, and can irritate humans. Dust mites need relative humidity levels above 50% to live, as they absorb water out of the air rather than drinking it. Dry the air, and dust mites die.

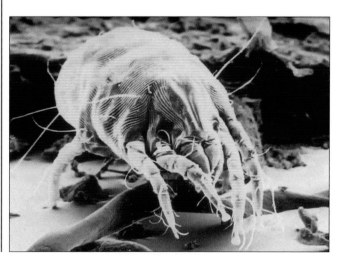

We have heard of a story of a doctor in West Virginia prescribing a SaniDry unit on his prescription pad! Now there's an enlightened doctor!

For more information, go to **www.housedustmite.com**

Now you know that finishing your basement makes sense. You know not to use organic materials to finish your basement. You have fixed any groundwater leakage and made sure the relative humidity is low.

You are ready to finish your basement!

Beautifully . . . Permanently . . . with Confidence

4

Let's do it!

You'll Love This!

Chapter 5

Walls that will last - even through the flood

What kind of basement walls you put in your basement will determine –

• How they look
• How much maintenance (painting, cleaning) they need
• How energy efficient they are
• If they will survive your **coming flood** event without being damaged

State of the *old* art

In 1984, if I had come into your home to finish your basement, you'd get the walls nearly everyone still gets – studs and drywall. Wood studs are put up against your foundation wall, fiberglass insulation with paper facing may or may not be installed, and then paper-faced drywall is installed over it. This is the detail that gets ruined and has to be ripped out every time it gets wet down there. What happens when you mix wood and or paper in a damp place? well, I think we adequately covered that one.

The case against metal studs in exterior walls

Some who think they know better try to use metal framing instead of wood so it will not rot or grow mold. It sounds logical and it makes sense. At Total Basement Finishing, when we need to use framing or mounting tracks, we use metal framing too. But we don't use metal studs on outside walls. Why? They're hundreds of times more thermally conductive than wood studs.

The outside of the walls is where we have to insulate. When we look at a wall assembly with metal studs with a Thermal Imaging camera, we see a cold stripe in the wall every 16 inches at each stud. A metal stud is the shape of a three-sided rectangle. Insulation is precut for a 14 ½" stud bay (studs 16" on center less the thickness of one stud). But since metal studs are hollow, insulation doesn't get tucked into the hollow of the stud, and this space allows air movement through the wall assembly or what we call a "thermal bypass". This can be overcome by ordering special wider insulation for metal studs, but most residential contractors don't know or think about this.

Heat moves by conduction and convection. Conduction is when heat moves through materials. Convection is when heat travels by air movement. Of the two, convection is the more important one. If you have the world's most insulated high tech window, it doesn't help you if it's open.

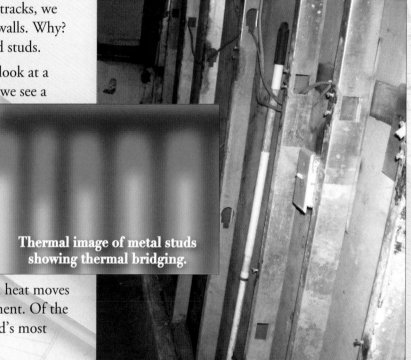

Drywall and stud walls get ruined by one leak event.

Thermal image of metal studs showing thermal bridging.

5

Stopping Fire and Ice

Fire stopping is important when constructing a finished basement wall. Most finished basement walls are constructed away from the foundation wall just ½" or so because the foundation wall is not straight, or many inches away from the foundation wall to hide, say, a sewer pipe. This leaves an air space between the finished, insulated wall, and the cold foundation wall.

This space causes two problems – it's a conductive highway for air movement and for heat and cold. If a fire were to start within a wall, the superheated air would travel up behind the wall in this space and catch the second floor on fire quickly. In addition, heated air above the dropped ceiling of your finished basement would hit the outside foundation wall, cool, and descend along the face of the foundation wall as it got heavier. This would push air up along the face of the backside of the finished wall and into the cavity above the ceiling. This creates a convective short circuit of your insulation.

The solution to both problems is fairly simple. At Total Basement Finishing, we install a firestop on the ceiling at the top of the walls before we install the walls. The firestop is a ½" code-approved material that will stop superheated air from a fire from going up from behind the walls, while also stopping airflow from above the ceiling from going down and up behind the walls. It's all in the details.

5

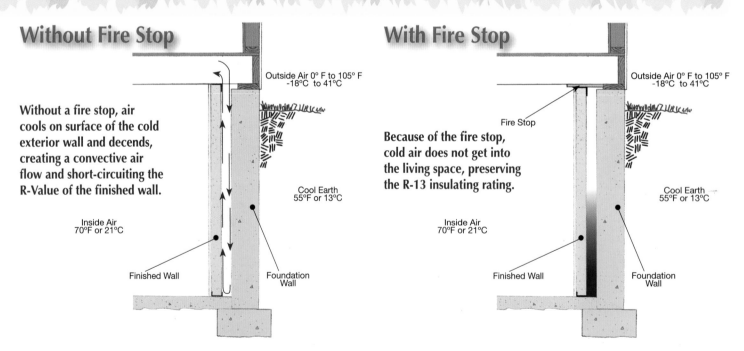

Without Fire Stop

Without a fire stop, air cools on surface of the cold exterior wall and decends, creating a convective air flow and short-circuiting the R-Value of the finished wall.

Outside Air 0° F to 105° F
-18°C to 41°C

Cool Earth
55°F or 13°C

Inside Air
70°F or 21°C

Finished Wall

Foundation Wall

With Fire Stop

Because of the fire stop, cold air does not get into the living space, preserving the R-13 insulating rating.

Outside Air 0° F to 105° F
-18°C to 41°C

Fire Stop

Cool Earth
55°F or 13°C

Inside Air
70°F or 21°C

Finished Wall

Foundation Wall

If wood studs rot and get moldy and metal studs cause heat loss, then what kind of studs should you have? Good question.

The answer is NO studs.

You only need studs if you're using a floppy, non-structural sheet material like drywall or paneling on their face.

TBF EverLast Walls are final.

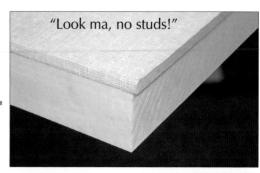
"Look ma, no studs!"

Total Basement Finishing has developed the perfect solution – EverLast Basement Wall Panels. EverLast Wall Panels have no studs. They are four foot wide panels of 2 ½" thick, high-density closed cell foam insulation, with a ½" cement board panel on the face, and a durable vinyl finish.

It's the new "State of the Art"

EverLast wall panels are better for your basement because they
- **Will never get moldy!**
- **Will never rot!**
- **Will not get ruined by a flood or leak – even if the water is a foot deep for a week!**
- **Will never need paint. You can hang anything on them no matter how heavy.**
- **You can patch a nail or screw hole easily!**
- **They have a continuous unbroken R-13 insulation layer!**
- **They won't dent like drywall or fiberglass and fabric walls!**
- **They are <u>very</u> washable!**
- **They're made for basement environments.**
    If you are looking to do it just once, these wall panels are what you need!

Note – Metal studs on INTERIOR basement walls such as between a utility room and the finished room in your basement, are fine because there is conditioned air on both sides of the wall and we are not worried about heat loss from one space to the other like we would be with an exterior wall.

R-Value

R-Value refers to resistance to conductive heat flow. Something with an R-1 rating means the material resists half the heat flow. R-2 would mean that the second "R" resists half of what gets through the R-1 material. So the first R resists 50% of the heat flow, and the second one resists 50% of what's left, therefore an R-2 material would resist 75% of the heat flow. R-3 resists 87.5% of the heat flow. R-4 resists 93.75%, and so on to R-13, which resists 99.99%. So the first R is the most important. All this supposes that the heat is on one side of the insulation material and the cold is on the other. If the cold air leaks to both sides, there is no heat flow for the insulation to resist. All insulation is tested for R-value in a laboratory condition in a closed cavity – with no airflow around the insulation at all. It's also inside information the fiberglass industry doesn't want anyone to know or think about. Air flows through cavities and fiberglass, and improperly installed fiberglass (which is common) easily. This is why it's important not to let the warm air from a basement get on the backside of the wall, because it renders the insulation useless.

5

Janesky's First Law of Conservation

"Doing a thing right so you don't have to do it over, will consume less resources and cost less than doing it twice or more."

Your TBF Basement will last 100 years. It is estimated that a basement finished with studs and drywall will have to be redone 5 times over 100 years (especially the flooring and the bottom half of the walls). That will cost more money, disruption, aggravation and will consume more natural and human resources.

The case against paint in a basement

Paint is no good is an environment that can get wet. Not unless you want to repaint all the time.

Latex paint is made from rubber, which comes from trees and is therefore organic. This means mold grows on paint. Besides that, when interior paint gets wet, it absorbs water, swells, bubbles, and loses its bond to the material it's on. And what needs to be painted anyways? Drywall and wood: materials we already know are not good for a basement in any case.

EverLast Wall Panels are prefinished. They never need to be painted or repainted. The durable vinyl surface is washable, and even pen ink comes off easily! Being underwater won't ruin the vinyl finish. Because it is not organic, mold will not grow on the walls. And the foam insulation is not organic either, so mold won't grow on it behind your walls.

Popularity contest

Studies show the two most popular interior colors are off-white and beige. They match any interior décor and never go out of style. TBF EverLast walls have both colors in them and are combined with a light random surface texture to expertly hide marks and wall shine. You won't ever get sick of the color, and you can dress up your room with furniture colors, art on the walls, even an area rug (which is easy to take away and dry or clean).

You'll Love This!

The EverLast walls are hard and durable

They won't dent like drywall. When the kids bang a drywall surface, it dents easily. You have to get out the spackle, apply a few coats, and then repaint the wall.

And since you can never get one spot of paint to match, you have to live with it or to repaint the entire wall. This will never happen with TBF walls. Hanging art or even a flat screen TV on the walls is no problemo with TBF walls. You don't even have to find a stud. Just put a screw or nail wherever you want it. And if you ever pull a nail out, all you have to do is patch the hole with a tiny bit of putty or even toothpaste – that's right, toothpaste. I assume that is readily available in your house! Another reason your walls won't rot!

Side Note

Insulation Integrity

Unlike a stud wall or fiberglass and fabric wall, TBF insulation is unbroken along the course of a wall. When you want it to last 100 years, it all matters.

Now that's strong! In fact by laboratory tests, it's many times stronger than studs and drywall!

5

Nobody like a moldy tuxedo!

It amazes me how products come out on the market that are presumed better because they are different. Sometimes they turn out to be different but no better at all. One basement finishing panel system has strings embedded in paint as a finish – it looks like stripes. Not only do the strings come off easily (the kids can pick at them and tear them off to the ceiling), but when exposed to a damp environment, these panels grow mold as fast as drywall. I don't get it. I watched the video, I read the brochure, and tested the product in a chamber for fourteen days. This is what happened to it. I still don't get it. Maybe I missed something…

Structural Insulated Panels

A sound technology. Finished basement walls are not structural walls. Since the foundation wall is the structural wall (holding up the structure above it) they don't need to be. But TBF EverLast walls are very strong – that's why they don't need any studs. In fact, they are based on a building system that is used to build exterior bearing walls with no studs, and roofs that span 30 feet with no rafters. The advantages of not having studs or rafters in these homes and buildings are impressive, as you can heat the building with a small fraction of the energy a conventionally built structure would cost.

Not all foam is equal.

As with any materials, there is good, better, and best. With foam, the lowest quality is a white "bead board". It has less R value per inch, and it's not as strong. It's like the packing material you see used in shipping. If used for a basement panel, it needs a board on the back to give it more rigidity. This material is individual beads of foam that are stuck together. The wall of one cell is not also the wall of the neighboring cell. There is a space between the beads to absorb water. In fact, when you put this material in a wet environment, it gains weight because it holds water. It's cheaper to buy, however. The best type of foam is high-density extruded closed cell foam. This material has individual closed cells with no spaces between the cells at all. This material can't gain any weight when put in a damp environment because it does not store water. That's good news if you don't want moldy damp walls!

Extra – Old News!

It's no new idea to not put organic materials in wet places. When you think about it, we have always done that. For example, our bathtub or shower uses ceramic tile or plastic or composite materials that don't get ruined by water. Our sinks and counters are stainless steel, porcelain, and formica laminates. We'd never use drywall in the shower or to make a wooden sink. This logic should be applied to a basement as well.

Take their breath away

Walls that breathe? One manufacturer says that their walls breathe and that's good. (It's an old marketing technique – take your products weakness and say why it's good). When you think about it, if they "breathe", that means air and water pass through them. From where to where? From the foundation walls to your living space, of course. Why do I want water vapor from the foundation walls in my living space? I don't know about you, but I don't. And if air passes through a wall, then what about the R (insulation) value? TBF EverLast panels block cold damp air from coming through. It makes more sense, don't you think?

One word – "Plastics"

You wouldn't finish your basement sanctuary with an inorganic panel that lasts 100 years and trim it out with <u>wood</u> baseboard and door casing, would you? You probably wouldn't want cold metal trim either. Plastic is the answer. Today, you can get plastic baseboard, casing, and other trim made of plastic that looks like wood. It meets our requirement because it will not get damaged when damp or wet, and it will not need paint (and re-painting) ever. This gives integrity to the space. Admittedly, the only vulnerable part of a TBF basement is the doors. They are still wood or masonite, which is a very fine wood particle board product. But the cost of inorganic interior doors is very high and nearly cost-prohibitive. Plastics and laminate-type products are a lot more expensive than wood. We're still working on that one.

5

Partition Walls

Walls between two interior spaces, such as between your finished room and a storage room or closet walls, are called "partition walls". Partition walls do not need to be insulated since they do not have an unconditioned, (cold outside space, on one side). There are two ways they can be constructed properly. First, an insulated studless TBF EverLast partition panel can be used. Even though it doesn't have any studs, this panel is stiff as a board. Well, stiffer, really. By independent laboratory test, it is 197% stronger than a stud wall with drywall on it. (In fact, the one-sided exterior panels are also substantially stronger than a stud wall with drywall as well.)

You'll Love This!

Two for one

The advantage: you get the same attractive, decorative, washable, finished look on both sides of the wall. When you walk into your storage room and turn around and look at the wall, you will see the same finish as on the finished side. This looks great, dresses up your storage room, and if ever decide to finish another room, this wall is already done!

The second way to do it is to build a metal stud wall and install TBF EverLast uninsulated panels on both sides of the wall to get a finished look on both sides. This will save you a bit of money and will look identical to the insulated two-sided partition panel. But aren't metal studs bad? Don't I need insulation? Remember, metal studs are heat loss highways only on exterior walls that are cold. An interior partition wall has indoor air on both sides, so we aren't worried about heat loss from one side to the other, and we don't need insulation in an interior wall.

The alternative is to have the back side of your finished walls look unfinished in the storage room. Some think this is okay. There will be studs showing, sharp metal edges, razor sharp screw points exposed, and wires hanging and exposed. The worst part is that with a fiberglass and fabric panel system, the fiberglass is exposed. That means that anything that touches the wall from the storage room side will get fiberglass fibers all over it. Do you know what that's like? If you try to brush it off, the fibers stick in your skin like little needles. And don't breathe it or get it on your eyes. Tell the kids too. And if something heavy enough falls against the wall, it can go right through the soft panel to the other side. Having partition walls with both sides finished looks and performs great, and it's safer.

Splash!

If you choose fiberglass and fabric walls, your cat will love it!

To illustrate how five different materials perform when wet, we hurled full 4' x 8' sheets in a pool! There no hiding on this test. Drywall and so called "moisture resistant" drywall absorbed about a half a gallon of water by weight in just 15 minutes, when we had to pull them out before they fell apart and wrecked the homeowner's pool! The plywood, representing any wood, also absorbed lots of water as expected and it also warped. The fiberglass and fabric panel started at just 22.8 pounds and sucked up so much water that it sunk in the pool! Four men could not pull it out because it weighed so much with water – an estimated 300 pounds! We had to let it drain as we took it out, and still it weighed a ton and fell apart. Hardly a material you'd want in your basement. The TBF EverLast Wall Panel weighed 95 pounds before testing. It didn't gain any weight from the pool, and it wasn't visibly affected by the water at all! The foam insulation, the finish, and the board looked just as good coming out of the pool at it did before it went in! It retained all its strength as two men stood on top of it as it floated in the pool like a big surfboard. There was only one winner, and it was clear. TBF EverLast panels will not get damaged or ruined when installed in your basement. If a leak happens, you'll never have to replace them! go to www.totalbasementfinishing.com/videos to see the video!

TBF EverLast Wall Panel!

Winner!

5

Fabric & Fiberglass Wall

Sunk and gained over 250 pounds of water!

Drywall - Gained Weight!

Sucked up over 1/2 gallon of water in 15 minutes!

Plywood- Gained Weight!

Gained over 8 pounds of water!

Don't finish it all!
Even unfinished space = finished space.

Remember that the price of your project depends on two things: how big the space is and what features and options you decide to have in it. You'll need some storage space in any home. For these reasons, you don't want to finish your WHOLE basement. Keep some space unfinished for storage. Otherwise you'll pack your upstairs closets, garage, and attic with the stored items you'd normally keep in the unfinished area of your basement. That doesn't really help you. And because you have a big storage space right through one door off your finished basement, you probably will not need any closets in your finished basement.

Electric Outlets

You should have an electrical outlet installed every 12 feet at least, and more in places you know you'll have items like computers, televisions, a flat screen TV on the wall, etc. installed. Phone jacks should be installed where you want them as well. Your TBF dealer can take care of all this for you. If you want to add a jack or outlet later, installing one is easy!

Dressing up <u>storage</u> space on a budget

Total Basement Finishing will make your finished basement look great. And you know you need some storage space. But is there a way to dress up the ugly walls in the storage space without investing in all out finished walls? Great question. And since so many people were interested in this, we developed a solution.

For about ¼ the price of the walls in the finished area, we can make the walls in your unfinished area look great too. ZenWall panels (patent pending) are ¼" thick panels with foil on the back surface and the great looking TBF washable vinyl surface on the face. The panels are 30" wide, and use a plastic trim between them. They are fastened with hidden fasteners drilled into the wall, so they can never come off.

ZenWall panels are a vapor barrier, thermal break (they do provide some insulation – remember the first "R" is the most important!) and make the walls look a world better than plain ugly concrete. They aren't fully finished walls. You can't install electrical outlets in them. They have a different trim configuration, and since they are mounted directly on the foundation, they will conform to the shape of the walls and not be perfectly straight. But at a fraction of the cost, they are just what the doctor ordered for your <u>unfinished</u> area!

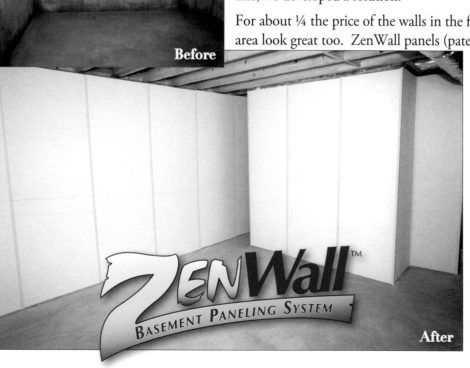

Before

After

ZenWall™
BASEMENT PANELING SYSTEM

5

Chapter 6

Beauty in Suspense - Ceilings that Last.

Now you have walls that will last, so you need a ceiling. A "dropped ceiling", also called a "suspended ceiling", is perfect for a basement. It allows easy access to all the pipes and wires that go to the rest of your home and are located in the ceiling. If there is ever a plumbing leak, you can access them and fix it, and you won't lose the whole ceiling like you would with a drywall ceiling.

The first thing we must have is adequate ceiling height per building code. Codes can vary a bit, but in general the code says 7 feet minimum. A percentage of the ceiling can be lower than that for girders and ducts to be boxed out. By now, you probably understand that if you buy "any old ceiling", you are probably going to get the cheapest design and materials available.

"Prestige" Ceiling Tile (hides marks)

"Linen" Ceiling Tile (looks bright & clean)

All Ceilings are not the Same

First of all, consider the tile size. A 2' X 4' tile doesn't look great in a small space. It may in a large commercial building, but in your home it looks cheap. That's because it is. 2' X 4' ceilings require less grid work and less labor. 2' X 2' tiles look much more elegant in a basement.

Next, a flush tile is said to be one where the surface of the tile you see is sitting on top of the grid. Flush tiles look cheap, and imperfections in tile and grid both pop out more. Instead, opt for a recessed tile. This tile has a notched edge that allows the tile to sit down about ¼" lower than the grid. This makes for a richer look and hides the grid a bit.

Apples & Oranges

Next, the quality of the tile itself is important. A cheap tile will sag under its own weight over the years. When a tile sags in the middle, it lifts in the corners and looks ugly. A high quality tile costs a bit more, but is well worth it TBF ceiling tiles have a 30 year warranty against sagging and mold.

Next, consider if the tile is made from paper or primarily from "mineral wool". Mineral wool is mined from the earth and not grown like paper. Paper tiles can grow mold, and while mineral wool tiles have a little paper content, they are highly resistant to mold.

2' X 2' recessed mineral wool tiles is what to get for the best look and long term performance. As far as color and texture, I love the bright, clean look of a pure white tile with no holes or dots in the surface . It looks clean and fresh and brightens up the basement the best. If you are using it for the kids who may throw stuff around and hit the ceiling or for a billiard room where sticks may hit the ceiling, then you may want to consider a textured tile that has a pattern of little holes and marks in the design. This will help hide future marks that the family adds to the ceiling.

6

No Thanks!

Yes, Please!

Little things can make a big difference!

Consider the perimeter of the ceiling against the wall. The basic commercial way to do it is to use an "L" channel against the wall for the grid and tiles to sit on. However this is… well… it's… as my young daughter used to say – "uggie".

Instead, a "crown" molding (plastic, of course) can be used against the wall. This is decorative, and if the right one is used, it substitutes for the "L" channel so the grid and tiles sit on it instead. It adds that nice touch that turns generic space into a luxury space and makes a house a home.

Ceilings can be used to box in ducts or girders. Often, however, this may be best accomplished using TBF wall panels that then have the ceiling run up to it.

"uggie"

Apples & Oranges

A beautiful Total Basement Finishing ceiling with crown molding and a girder boxed in.

Let there be Light!

"Fluorescent" Light

"Can" Light

Of course, you will need lighting in your basement ceiling. You have two basic choices; fluorescent lighting or down lighting, also called "can" lights. Both are recessed into the dropped ceiling. Fluorescent lighting gives you the most light. It's great for when you are doing a project, or for a kids playroom when you want to fill the space with bright white light. Can lighting usually uses incandescent bulbs. They offer a much different look and feel than fluorescent lights, with a warm local light under the fixture. Can lights can be dimmed with a special switch to set the mood in your basement. They're great for watching TV, or just relaxing. Compact fluorescent (CF) bulbs last many times longer than regular incandescent ones, and you can get 60 watts of light while burning only 13 watts or so. It sounds like a great idea, and if I were you I'd change as many of the bulbs in my home as I could to compact fluorescent bulbs. When they first came out, they gave off a ghastly blue-white light, but now they are much better. You may not be able to tell the difference from the bulbs you've grown used to. Over the life of the bulb, you can save $60 or so in electricity. If you install them outside, CF bulbs don't light up instantly when they are cold. If you had outside lights on timers that go on every night automatically, then definitely use CF bulbs there. On your front porch when you may want to flick the light on instantly, stick with a regular bulb. You can add CF bulbs in your can lights, but most are not dimmable. The technology is changing and one day soon there will be readily available dimmable CF bulbs. You may be able to find them now if you look hard enough.

"Dimmer" Switch

6

Choose both!

It's amazing how your basement can look like totally different space depending on how it's lit. I'm a fan of having both fluorescent and can lights in your basement. With the flick of two switches, you can change the way it looks and alter the mood dramatically. You can put the fluorescent lights in the middle area of the room and add a can light every 8 feet or so around the perimeter. The building code says you need a light for every 100 square feet of dropped ceiling. But I'd go with more than that — a light fixture for every 60 square feet of ceiling. It costs more to have both, so it's up to you, your budget, and what you really want your new space to be. You can always supplement the lighting with table lamps or floor lamps.

Chapter 7

Flooring for the long haul - despite the water.

Of all the surfaces in your basement, the floor is the one that is most vulnerable to water damage when the leak happens. The water will get onto and then under the floor and sit there for a long time before it dries out. It will get sucked up into wood floors or carpets like a sponge and ruin them. I have seen many hardwood floors buckled like beach sand at low tide. Laminate floors are simply particle board with a thin plastic finish laminated to the top surface. When they get wet, they swell at the edges between the boards. When they dry, they don't regain their previous shape and are ruined. Just one plumbing leak will take you out.

Carpet, and carpet with padding, will soak up water like a giant sponge and will have to be taken out when it gets wet.

You don't need a huge leak to ruin these types of flooring. Water vapor passing through your porous concrete floor in a slow, invisible, unending stream from the damp earth below is enough to cause buckling, and will cause moisture to get trapped under your flooring making it smell moldy from the rotting flooring underneath. Of course, there is a solution. Several choices, in fact.

ThermalDry Floor Matting

The ThermalDry Basement Floor Matting comes in a carpeted or tiled finish. ThermalDry is modular floor tiles that snaps together. Each tile has raised pegs on the bottom that create an air space under the floor. This prevents water from condensing under the floor, and it creates a thermal break by putting a space between your feet and the cold, hard, concrete floor.

The carpet and tile is water resistant. When you have a flood, just dry the place out, which is much easier with the air space under the floor, and the carpet or tile is not ruined. A few tiles can easily be popped up to blow air under the floor with a fan when needed for drying up after a leak.

Mocha Carpet

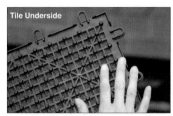
Tile Underside

Charcoal

Mocha

Canyon Beige Tile

ThermalDry®
Basement Floor Matting™

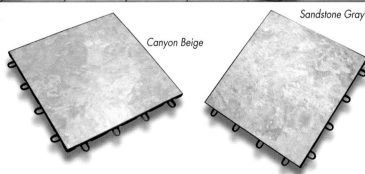
Canyon Beige

Sandstone Gray

7

For wall-to-wall carpet installation

For those that insist on their favorite pink color or a Berber carpet, be careful not to lay carpet down on a cold, hard, damp basement floor. Instead, ThermalDry is available in plain unfinished so that you can install a wall-to-wall carpet on top of it. By not having the carpet on the concrete, it will be warmer, dryer, and better smelling, Additionally it will last twice as long as it would otherwise in a basement.

Advantages of Modularity

If you ever have a stain or damage to one spot in the floor, in one minute you can replace that tile with another, (or switch it for one from a closet or under furniture). You can't do that with wall-to-wall carpet or any other tile! I love this feature. We all have high traffic areas in the room, and when we change our carpet we usually do so because one area is looking tired. With these tiles you can get many times the life out of the floor because you can change or relocate the tired tiles easily – and they won't be affected by water or dampness.

Another advantage is that you can mix and match the pattern of tiled areas and carpeted areas. You can tile the high-traffic areas and carpet the rest.
It makes for a custom architectural look, and it's easy.

Modular design allows tiles to 'snap' together for easy relocation!

7

Fool Your Friends

Yet another good option is a wood floor that is totally inorganic. This means it's not wood at all, it just looks like it. MillCreek Flooring is a Total Basement Finishing exclusive, and has the warm, earthy look of wood, but is all-plastic. While it does not create a space under the floor like the ThermalDry Flooring does, it will not be affected by water at all. When there is a leak, you will not have to worry about your floor. Just fix the leak and dry the area, and you're good.

MillCreek Flooring comes in planks like real wood and has a tongue and groove design to lock them together. They are installed on a 2 mm

MillCreek
FLOORING™
Sensible & Beautiful Basement Floors

thick foam underlayment like a laminate floor which makes it quiet and even softens the floor. MillCreek is a great option. But don't expect it to be as hard as hardwood though. If there is going to be a lot of rough activity in the basement I'd use the modular ThermalDry. If it's a family room space for games and TV and you love the look of wood, you'll love MillCreek Flooring. And you'll still love it after a plumbing leak!

7

Caveat Emptor
(Buyer Beware)

CAUTION

Apples & Oranges

In the Big Box stores, you'll see a underlayment "Made just for basements" that is 2' square tiles of chipboard (Oriented Strand Board, OSB) with a dimpled plastic on the bottom. They recommend it for laying carpet on top of in your basement. The idea is that it creates a space between the floor and your carpet for warmth. The plastic will stop water vapor from getting to your floor. Don't buy it. There are a few big problems. First, as you know it's wood. Even worse it's chipboard. One

Forget real wood on a basement floor!

wetting event and you'll be replacing the subfloor, which means you'll have to remove the finished floor to do it. When it does get wet, it swells, especially since the little dimples in the plastic under the chipboard are facing up and fill with water. If you were an insect under the floor and looked up at the joints, you'd see ¼" of chipboard exposed between the tiles. All the moisture under the floor is being absorbs into the end grain of the chipboard and it swells. If you have a thin carpet with no padding, you may even be able to see the outline of each tile through the carpet where it has swollen with the moisture that has soaked into the chip

7

"Repeat after me: Wood + Water = Bad."

Imagine Your Basement As Your Favorite Room In Your Home!

7

AS SEEN ON
TV

Total Basement Finishing was featured on the Ron Hazelton Show airing nationwide- where we did a complete basement waterproofing and finishing project.

RON HAZELTON'S
HOUSECALLS

www.ronhazelton.com/

Additionally one of our projects was featured on the show "American Builder".

★AMERICAN BUILDER

www.cn8.tv/channel/channelhome. asp?IChannelID=1012

Chapter 8

Window Dressing

Basement windows

They're small, ugly, and easy to overlook during your basement improvement project. If you leave them the way they are, they will stick out like a sore thumb while the rest of your new finished basement space looks great.

Basement windows and associated window wells are an eyesore. They were chosen by the builder because they're cheap, and quite frankly, not a lot of thought went into them. If your home is older, when it was built there wasn't much of a basement window selection and fuel cost a small fraction of what it does today.

Most basement windows do not seal very well. Since the basement has low air pressure (sucking air in), the cold winter air or warm humid summertime air is pulled into the basement. This is a no win situation. Either way, it costs you more in heating, cooling, and dehumidification costs.

Basement windows have a tough job because they're down close to the ground or in a window well – both damp environments. Metal-framed windows rust, wood windows rot, and they are impossible to keep painted. In addition to the fact that they leak air, single pane glass is an energy waster.

The time to deal with your basement windows is when you're having the basement finished. This way the interior trim can be wrapped around the new window.

Isn't there something better?

There is!

EverLast Basement Windows

EverLast Basement Windows are all vinyl: the perfect material for a basement window because it won't rot, rust, or ever need paint. Ever-Last Windows have double pane glass and good weather stripping for warmth and comfort. The sashes slide open and even come out easily – a feature you should not use unless you're cleaning the outside of the windows. EverLast Windows look great and will stay that way. Since they slide into an existing opening in the foundation, the glass area may be a bit smaller than what you have now, especially in a poured concrete wall.

EverLast™
Windows

They Aren't Submarine Windows!

If you have a window well that takes on water against the basement window, it will leak in. The fix is not included in any contractor's scope of work unless specifically called out. And new EverLast Windows won't solve this problem. Your local Basement Systems dealer has the answer. Ask them about it.

What would need to be done besides the obvious (extend downspouts, keep grade pitched away, and keep your gutters clean) is to establish a drain from the window well to an interior perimeter drain like WaterGuard. This way, if water fills the window wells, even a new one, it will drain away before it fills up against the glass and leaks into the basement.

A flooding window well will ruin your finished basement. We have the solution!

8

What Are You Looking At?

If your window wells are rusty, ugly, or open at the top, they can be dramatically improved. Window wells without covers let in leaves, debris, rain, and gutter overflow water. The dirt bottom allows weeds to grow and mud to splash up onto your windows. All this makes for a pretty lousy view from inside the basement – which is the space you want to improve.

You'll Love This!

The Answer is a Great Product: SunHouse Basement Window Enclosures

The light-colored SunHouse Basement Window Enclosures, features a sturdy, clear cover that fits nicely and a bottom that prevents weed growth, keeps leaves, debris, and rain out. One of the SunHouse's best benefits is that with the clean, light-colored bottom, a lot more sunlight bounces into your basement and brightens up a space where we can use *all the natural light we can get.*

8

The more natural light in your basement, the better. You can see why we call it a "SunHouse".

What a difference!

SunHouse™
Basement Window Enclosure

Looks Great!

The SunHouse Basement Window Enclosure really dresses up what used to be an eyesore.
Bright and clean.

The cover keeps dirt, debris, and weeds from getting in your SunHouse!

Keep Windows Closed!

Even though EverLast basement windows are smooth-operating windows and are easy to open, I can think of no reason to ever open a window in a basement other than to pass a long object, such as a ladder, through. In cooler weather, we want to keep cold air out. In warm weather we want to keep warm air out to avoid condensation problems.

Fire Escapes

If you are installing a bedroom in your basement, the building code will probably require an "egress" window. An egress window is one that is big enough to climb out of if there was a fire. It will likely need to have a big window well around it if it's deep in the ground, and that window well will need a ladder or steps so you can climb out in an emergency.

SCAPE**WEL**®
Window Well System

If you decide to have a bedroom in the basement, expect to put an egress window in as a fire escape.

Building Codes

Some codes are requiring egress windows even when the finished basement has no bedroom. Most homeowners would hope that they don't have to install an egress window with their project because they can add around $5000 each to your project. To put one in, you have to dig a huge hole with an excavator machine. That means the yard is dug up and any utilities, landscaping and underground pipes have to be considered. A drain in the bottom of the hole must be established so the big new window well doesn't fill up with water. Then a big concrete saw cuts a large hole in your basement wall – a dusty proposition usually. Once this is completed the window frame and window can be installed. Finally the big egress window well is put in and backfilled with stone aggregate for draining. It's disruptive, and it's not cheap.

The good news is it gets a lot of natural light into your basement and it makes it feel like a warmer, larger space. And, of course if there were a fire….

An alternative is to use the hatchway steps as an exit. Hatchway steps are common in the Northeast and less so in the Midwest. They allow access to the outside via a concrete stairway and hatch door. If you must install an egress window, you may consider installing hatchway steps instead, since it costs about the same as an egress window. The disadvantage is that you don't get any light into the basement that way, but you can have access for moving objects in and out of the basement.

8

A hatchway is an alternative to an egress window well.

Chapter 9

Custom Features

A Home Theater – The luxury of the 2000's

In the sixties and seventies, a basement bar seemed to be a luxury many had installed. Then playrooms were popular for the kids to hang out. While some still want those things, as our population ages, a home theater seems to be more and more popular. Some call a loveseat in front of a sizable TV a home theater. Fair enough. Some will enjoy a big flat screen television on the wall with comfy living room furniture. Others with a bigger budget go big.

Before

A projector mounted from the ceiling can shoot a nine foot picture on the wall in high definition or Blu-Ray, which is a better picture still. The screen is simply a framed white board, but velvet curtains and art deco sconce lighting fixtures on each side give it that authentic movie theater look. Surround sound speakers make the electronics package complete.

Seating is available with recliners and the all important cup holders. The leather wipes off easy. For an even more dramatic experience, subwoofers can be installed under each seat! (Remember going to the movies with "Sensaround"!) A second row can be elevated to have a great view from anywhere.

9

What is HDTV and Blu-Ray?

High Definition Television, or HDTV, refers to a TV signal that displays a much higher resolution than the standard definition television (SDTV) screen. As HDTV screens become popular, the shortcomings of SDTV have become obvious. HDTV shows a much crisper, more detailed picture.HDTV televisions will not improve the picture showing from SDTV channels- only HDTV ones. HDTV signals are going to become the federal government standard for all TV beamed over the airwaves by February of 2009. Computers and video game systems are also becoming HDTV complaint.

"Blu-ray" Disc (also known as Blu-ray or BD) is a video and data storage format made especially to store and display HDTV television without losing video quality. A Blu-ray disk can hold more than five times as much as a normal DVD can at the same size. Blu-ray gets its name from the beam it projects onto the disk. Unlike normal red beams used by traditional DVDs, a Blu-ray uses a blue laser beam to read and write. The shorter wavelength of the beam (405 nanometers instead of 650) increases the data that can be stored and read from the disk significantly.

A small stage built in front of the screen makes for a cool look and provides a place for the kiddies to perform their latest acts for the parents and grandparents. While Total Basement Finishing dealers do not install home theaters, there are outfits that do. You can call them after you have your basement finished and ready. These electronics are expensive and someone who knows what they're doing should set it all up and program everything. And the extra work required to build stages, raise a back row of seats, and install curtains can add up. It all depends on what you want. But one thing is for sure. If you make this kind of investment and it all gets ruined when there's a leak, it makes it that much more of a tragedy. They say the size of a problem depends how much money it costs to fix! Home theaters look great in TBF basements, and you can rest easy knowing it won't smell like mold..

You Gotta' Go — Basement Bathrooms

You can add a bathroom to your basement – a half bath with a toilet and sink or a full bath with a toilet, sink, and shower. It depends if you just want to take care of business without going upstairs or if someone is living in the basement. As any builder will tell you, the two most expensive rooms in a home are the kitchen and bathroom. There is a lot of construction detail in these rooms that make it all work. For a bathroom, you need plumbing supply pipes coming off your existing ones and run to the toilet, sink, and shower. You need drain pipes from the toilet, sink, shower, and a vent pipe. The trouble is the toilet and shower are sitting on the concrete floor, so the floor has to be jack hammered open to install the drains underneath it. Plumbers usually don't like to jackhammer. To solve this problem, various drain systems have been devised that do not require jack hammering. An above the concrete floor vessel with a pump in it substitutes for a sewage ejection pump that goes below the floor in a liner, similar to a sump pump. There is no jack hammering, but you have to raise the bathroom floor up on a step, or raise just the shower and toilet. You wind up seeing plumbing pipes too. I am not a big fan of this method, and I'll jackhammer the floor open to get everything below it and out of sight. (If you're lucky, you have plumbing already below the floor for the drains. This way you just have to connect to them and don't need a pump to pump it up. If your sewer or septic ran out of the basement wall above the basement floor at a higher elevation.) If you're super lucky, those drain hook-ups for your toilet and sink were installed at the right spot and there's no jack hammering at all. If you live in Ohio in a newer home you may be so fortunate, but it's not likely unless your builder was a visionary. Like I said, not likely. You also need a separate electric circuit for the bathroom on a Ground Fault Circuit Interrupter (GFCI), according to code, so nobody gets shocked in the wet bathroom environment. Bathroom fans, towel bars & mirrors will all add to the costs. As far as flooring, the MillCreek inorganic wood flooring is ideal for a bathroom. You can add throw rugs if you like. A basement bathroom can be an economy version with a pedestal sink and toilet and that's it, or it can be more luxurious and rich than any bathroom you have upstairs. It all depends on your budget and what you want. You can spend $7,000 or $17,000 or more on it.

A sewage ejection pump to be installed below the floor.

Basement Doors

The most common type of door is a six panel door; they're readily available and the price is right. You can go nuts with fancy doors, but the six panel is standard.

Here are a few other ideas –

Double doors – Double doors allow you to move furniture in and out easily and can allow easier access to a wide closet.

French door – A French door has glass panes that run the full height of the door. It costs more, of course, but it can be a nice design element and allow more light between finished spaces. It can also make a small room look bigger.

Bi-fold door – I personally don't like the clumsy operation of these doors, but they are good where swing space is limited.

Louver door – A louver door allows air to pass through it. It's good for utility rooms with furnaces, water heaters and boilers, or for a "home theater equipment" closet where heat may be generated.

Doors and their jambs are one area that uses wood in your basement even with TBF. The reason is that inorganic doors just are not available without paying an absolute fortune. Most doors come primed only, and louver doors are usually available in bare wood only, so you'll have to paint the doors.

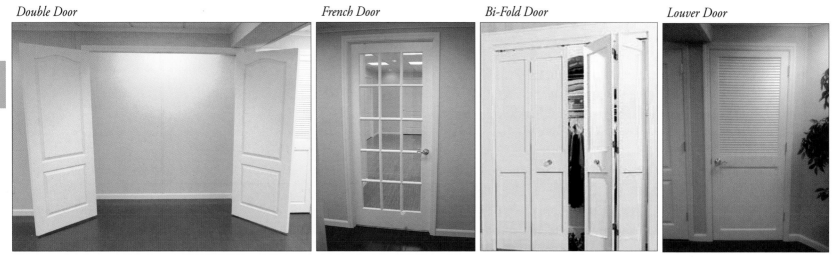

Double Door   *French Door*   *Bi-Fold Door*   *Louver Door*

9

Door hardware

If a contractor doesn't mention the standard of what you are getting, then you are getting the cheapest stuff available. In the case of door hardware, the quality of the mechanism and the finish varies a lot between brands. A pet peeve of mine is tarnished door knobs. A good quality hardware set will have a high quality finish that will last longer than you do.

You don't want cheap hardware that will tarnish!

Quality hardware will never tarnish.

Levers are nicer

I like levers over knobs. If your hands are full, you can still open the door. And they are great for small children and the elderly too.

Personalize and decorate with art

By choosing what you hang on the walls, you can establish the feel of your space. You can add color that can easily be changed. You will have no problem hanging anything on a TBF wall – you don't even have to find a stud. Just put a nail or screw wherever you want. When you pull it out, patch the little hole with putty or even toothpaste!

9

Sweet Cedar Scents

When you finish your basement you can get very creative with the design elements. As I mentioned, most people don't need much for closets because you have a storage area in the next room. But sometimes a closet can be a way to box a utility in, like a sump pump for example. Other times it can avoid an odd shaped room. A regular closet, can be made into a cedar closet to store winter clothes in summer, and summer clothes in winter. This frees up space in upstairs closets so because they don't have to carry the entire annual burden. And if you design it with cedar it smells oh so good!

9

◀ *Wire shelves let you see what's on them, lets light through and they don't collect dust!*

Custom Lighting

You can customize light fixtures for a unique look. Wall sconce fixtures, or light fixtures that hang from the ceiling are ways to do that. They are available in literally thousands of styles to suit your taste. And don't worry: they can be installed later if you decide to dress up the basement because wires can easily be installed behind the TBF EverLast wall or above the ceiling.

For an extra fee, you can have some of the electrical outlets put on a wall switch at the bottom of the stairs. Then when you come down, you can turn on lamps with the wall switch. It beats "The Clapper" any day.

For super high-tech lighting in closets, you can have a door jamb switch installed. When you open the door, the light automatically goes on and when you close it, it goes off. A fluorescent strip light can be installed inside the closet on the wall over the door.

Billiard Rooms and Basement Bars

You can transform your basement into a billiard room with a bar easily with furniture from your local pool table retailer. Many of them carry a whole line of cool bars that stand alone as independent furniture. In my opinion, this is the way to go instead of a permanent built-in bar. If you ever get tired of it, you can just take it out and put something else in. They will also carry a whole line of accessory furniture to pool tables, such as game tables for cards, chess, backgammon, bumper pool, etc. It's a lot of fun walking through the showroom and seeing what they have. And with a healthy new TBF basement, you have a blank canvas to fill!

9

Stair Treatment Options

The easy way to treat the stairs is to run a wall to the end of them on both sides. Then a surface-mounted stair rail can be installed on the wall.

Another way is to install what we call a "Nevada Window". I bet you can guess why we call it that! A Nevada window opens up the stairwell and brings light in. When you're coming down the stairs they don't look so long since you get a view before you are at the bottom. It also adds interest and design from down in the basement. Another option is an open stair rail. This looks great all around.

These options will cost more than the simpler straight walls along the stairwell. The steps themselves take some thought. First, if they're open riser stairs, then you'll want to close them and probably carpet them. If they are already closed riser stairs, then you may find that painting them and adding carpet pads to the treads will be adequate. Other times, painting the sides of the steps and four inches out onto the steps from the sides while running a hemmed carpet runner down the middle makes for a nice look.

It's up to you.

What you choose to have in your basement and what size it is determines the cost. One basement may be a simple rectangle layout with one door and a plain stairwell. That could be half the cost of another of the same size with closets, open stair rail, multiple windows, window wells, both types of lighting, and two main rooms instead of one. It's all up to you. Work with your designer to get a space that will fit your budget and that will make you happy.

Surface mounted stair rail.

"Nevada Window"

9

Chapter 10

Summary – What to do in one page or less

TBF Total BASEMENT Finishing

From Basement to Beautiful!™

If money is no object – do this $$$

Money **is** an object. Okay, it is. But only if you expected to pay cash for your basement finishing project. Most people don't pay cash for an automobile – they finance it. There are lots of options to get your project done – a home equity loan, or your TBF dealer can finance it for you and you can make comfortable monthly payments. No matter how much you spend, you want it to last. We can't predict when a plumbing or other leak will happen, but we can predict that it will. Of course, all known groundwater leaks will happen again and must be fixed properly before finishing your basement. Have your basement finished with Total Basement Finishing products that are <u>truly</u> water, moisture, and mold-resistant.

A basement on a budget $

A simple rectangular room at the bottom of the stairs. EverLast wall panels, six panels door(s), one type of lighting (fluorescent or can lights), TBF Prestige ceiling tiles, and ThermalDry carpeted flooring. If you have windows, change them to EverLast windows. How much? Everyone wants to know how much! Well, there is so many "depends" that I just can't say without you talking to your TBF representative about it. He or she will take you shopping for the project and all the features you want with an exact price. But put it this way; for the price of a small car, you can have a more beautiful space for living that will last 100 years! It sounds like a bargain to me. And at TBF, estimates and consultations are FREE!

A custom basement $$$$

Do the above plus consider a SaniDry Basement Air System, both types of ceiling lighting, SunHouse Basement Window Enclosures, ZenWall paneling in the storage area, an open stair rail or Nevada Window. Consider mixing the flooring with tile and carpet, and all the custom feature you want. Your TBF representative will work with you to make it what you want.

Cost the sky's the limit. $14,000 to $114,000. The price depends on how big of an area you finish, what features, and options you decide to have in it - and that's up to you. You get what you pay for, and if you do it right, it will last.

10

"Finishing"

I hope this book has helped you. If it sounds like a commercial, well, so be it. If there were better wall, floor or ceiling products for basements, as the owner of TBF, I'd have them. I feel I am on a mission. I am David and they are Goliath. This industry has big corporations that are selling inferior stuff and telling people how great they are, and that bothers me. Then there are thousands of small operators who don't understand the issues unique to a basement because they've thought about it. Now that you know the facts, you can make up your own mind. We believe our innovations will help people like you and make basements better. And remember, you get your money back on healthy, clean, basement space. If anyone finds any facts in this book to be in error, please let us know. Contact us through our web site at **www.totalbasementfinishing.com** Our good reputation is important to us, and giving our customers good advice and the service to go along with it, is how we maintain it. Enjoy your newly finished space – forever! In addition, the Basement Systems Network includes crawl space repair contractors in 48 states installing the CleanSpace System, and Foundation Supportworks dealers who fix settling, cracking foundations and bowing basement walls.

10

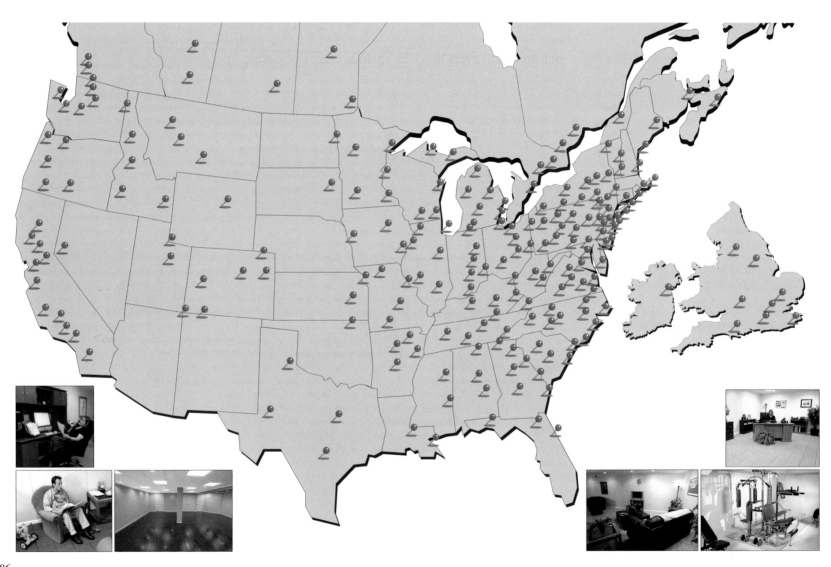

About the Author

After five years as a carpenter and builder, Larry Janesky founded Basement Systems Inc. in 1987 to provide basement waterproofing services to existing homes. He soon learned that there was much room for improvement in the industry, and he set out to make those improvements. He has since patented 24 products, with more pending and even more in various stages of design and development.

Larry is currently the president of the world's largest basement waterproofing and crawl space repair dealer network, Basement Systems Inc., that specializes in developing and providing products that result in dry below-ground environments. The company has won three business ethics awards, two consumer education awards, and multiple quality and innovation awards in the past five years. In 2006, Basement Systems was voted one of the "10 Best Places to Work in Connecticut" by its employees.

Larry has been invited to a number of industry conventions to discuss his research and solutions. Larry has trained thousands of people over the last 16 years on basement waterproofing and crawl space repair. His articles have been published in *Fine Homebuilding* magazine, *Permanent Buildings and Foundations* magazine, and other publications. He wrote the book on dirt crawl spaces entitled, "Dirt Crawl Spaces: America's Housing Epidemic" and its successor "Crawl Space Science."

Larry enjoys his free time in rural Connecticut with his son, Tanner, daughters Chloe and Autumn, and his lovely wife, Wendy. There he also builds and rides on his motocross track and ATV trails.

You can read more about Basement Systems Inc., basement waterproofing, below-grade environments, and the CleanSpace® Crawl Space Encapsulation® System at www.basementsystems.com.

Notes

_____

_____

_____

_____

_____

_____

_____

_____

_____

_____

_____

_____

_____